KU-334-768

#11469588

ASPECTS OF CIVIL ENGINEERING CONTRACT PROCEDURE

THIRD EDITION

R.J. MARKS, F.R.I.C.S.,
R.J.E. MARKS, BSc., C.Eng. M.I.C.E.

and

ROSEMARY JACKSON, LL.B., Barrister

PERGAMON PRESS

OXFORD · NEW YORK · TORONTO · SYDNEY · FRANKFURT

U.K.	Pergamon Press Ltd., Headington Hill Hall, Oxford OX3 0BW, England
U.S.A.	Pergamon Press Inc., Maxwell House, Fairview Park, Elmsford, New York 10523, U.S.A.
CANADA	Pergamon Press Canada Ltd., Suite 104, 150 Consumers Road, Willowdale, Ontario M2J 1P9, Canada
AUSTRALIA	Pergamon Press (Aust.) Pty. Ltd., P.O. Box 544, Potts Point, N.S.W. 2011, Australia
FEDERAL REPUBLIC OF GERMANY	Pergamon Press GmbH, Hammerweg 6, D–6242 Kronberg-Taunus, Federal Republic of Germany

Copyright © 1985 R.J. Marks, R.J.E. Marks, R. Jackson

All Rights Reserved. No part of this publication may be reproduced, stored in a retrieval system or transmitted in any form or by any means: electronic, electrostatic, magnetic tape, mechanical, photocopying, recording or otherwise, without permission in writing from the publisher

First edition 1965

Second edition 1978

Third edition 1985

Library of Congress Cataloging in Publication Data
Marks, R. J. (Raymond John)
Aspects of civil engineering contract procedure.
  (Pergamon international library of science,
technology, engineering, and social studies)
Bibliography: p.
Includes index.
1. Civil engineering—Contracts and
specifications—Great Britain. 2. Civil
engineering—Contracts and specifications. I. Marks,
R.J.E. (Richard J.E.) II. Jackson, R. (Rosemary)
III. Title. IV. Series.
KD 1641.M37   1985   343.41′078624   84–25569
                          344.10378624
British Library Cataloguing in Publication Data
Marks, R.J.
Aspects of civil engineering contract procedure.—3rd
ed./R.J. Marks, R.J.E. Marks and
R. Jackson—(Pergamon international library)
1. Civil engineering—Contracts and
specifications—England
I. Title   II. Marks, R.J.E.   III. Jackson, R.
624   TA181.G7

ISBN 0–08–031637–9
ISBN 0–08–031638–7 Pbk

Printed in Great Britain by A. Wheaton & Co., Ltd., Exeter

PREFACE TO THE THIRD EDITION

The legal sections of this book in the first two editions were contributed by Mr. A. A. Grant, Barrister, now a Master of the Supreme Court, Queen's Bench Division. In this edition they have been revised and added to by Miss Rosemary Jackson, Barrister. Mr. Richard Marks has rewritten the chapter on Overseas Contracts and made revisions elsewhere to the parts originally contributed by the late Mr. P.W. Helson.

The authors would like to thank Mr. Gilgunn-Jones of Pergamon Press and his staff for their painstaking and patient expertise.

CONTENTS

TABLE OF CASES

TABLE OF STATUTES

CHAPTER 1

INTRODUCTION

Scope of Civil Engineering Work

The scope of civil engineering work is vast, and encompasses the whole of man's endeavour to shape and improve his physical environment. Roads, railways, docks, dams, land reclamation, bridges, power stations and pipe lines are all the responsibility of the civil engineer, together with tunnels, sea defences and sewerage schemes. He will also be called upon to design and carry out the construction of the foundations and structure of large buildings.

The design and supervision of civil engineering works are usually carried out by firms of consulting engineers or by professional civil engineers in the public service, and the organization and execution of the works by public works contractors. There is still a clear separation of functions, for, although most of the larger contractors have their own design and drawing offices, the men who staff them are not usually concerned with contract and site management. When these firms offer clients a combination of consultancy services with contracting, it is still likely that the client will appoint a civil engineer in private practice to negotiate for him and protect his interests.

Often civil engineering and building works will overlap and intermingle. Both these construction industries use the same materials, similar plant, and share part of the same labour force. The major contracting firms undertake both civil engineering and building works, and will be members of both the separate national federations of civil engineering and building trade employers. As the general trend is towards specialization in one particular class of work such as reinforced concrete work, excavation and demolition, piling, tunnelling and marine work, these major firms are usually composed of specialist departments, sometimes autonomous, who confine their operations to a particular class of work; and much the same is true of consultants in private practice and the public service.

Despite this steady trend towards specialization, efforts are being made to achieve more collaboration between sections of the construction industries. The possibility of a common form of contract for both building and civil engineering works is being considered, and an attempt is being made to bring a degree of uniformity to the wage structure and working conditions in both industries. Civil engineering and building works are often undertaken jointly on a single site and different methods and procedures may produce misunderstanding and friction.

Forms of Contract

The form of contract most used in the United Kingdom for civil engineering works is entitled *Conditions of Contract and Forms of Tender, Agreement and Bond for use in connection with Works of Civil Engineering Construction*, 5th ed., and is commonly known as the I.C.E. contract, and will be so called throughout this book. It is published jointly by the institution of Civil Engineers, the Association of Consulting Engineers and the Federation of Civil Engineering Contractors. The government departments mostly use the *General Conditions of Government Contract for Building and Civil Engineering Works*, generally known and referred to hereafter as GC/Works/1.

Abroad, contract procedures vary, and these will be dealt with briefly in the final chapter, but it should be mentioned here that the international federations of consulting engineers and civil engineering contractors have sponsored an international form of contract which is already printed in several languages.

This international contract is largely based on the I.C.E. contract and shares much of its wording, clause numbering and intent.

The civil engineer will find that sometimes he must use a building form of contract. Indeed, those engineers who specialize in structural engineering will sometimes find themselves almost exclusively concerned with the standard forms of building contract issued under the authority of the Joint Contracts Tribunal. The constituent bodies of the Tribunal include the Royal Institute of British Architects, the Building Trades Employers Confederation, the Royal Institution of Chartered Surveyors, the Association of Consulting Engineers, representatives of sub-contractor's associations and of the local authority associations. Some of the forms are applicable where quantities form part of the contract. These will be called the "J.C.T. quantities contract" wherever referred to. There are two versions, one for the use of local authorities, and the other for the use of limited companies and individuals. There are several important differences between the I.C.E. contract, the J.C.T. contract with quantities, and GC/Works/1, but they have a basic similarity. This book will deal chiefly with the I.C.E. contract, but information about other contracts will be given when they differ from the I.C.E. contract.[1]

Parties to the Contract

Contracts for works of construction are normally made between two parties, the "Employer" (who commissions the work) and the "Contractor". The employer will almost certainly be a corporate body such as a government department, local authority, statutory board or limited liability company. Before the Corporate Bodies' Contracts Act, 1960 came into force a corporation could only enter into a contract under seal. It is no longer essential for the contract to be under seal, but it is still customary for contracts involving large sums of money to be sealed. The benefits of making a contract under seal are

[1] See p. 50–51 for the Contract sponsored by the Association of Consultant Architects.

discussed later in this chapter and in Chapter 2, which describes in more detail the formation of contracts.

Special difficulties arise when work is carried out for unincorporated bodies such as clubs and societies. The members of an unincorporated members' club are not liable upon contracts entered into by the trustees or committee of management of the club unless the contracts are within the scope of the authority given by the club's rules, or are expressly sanctioned or subsequently ratified by the members. Trade unions and employers' associations, however, although unincorporated, may enter into contracts and accept what amounts to corporate liability and can sue and be sued in their own name.[1]

Apart from his obligation to pay and give possession of the site to the contractor, the standard forms of contract delegate the employer's other positive duties and powers to his representative. This representative may be either a consulting engineer in private practice, or the principal of a specialist department within the employer's organization. These alternative relationships with the employer have never been held to make any difference to the agent's contractual standing. The consulting engineer, in addition to his duties as agent of the employer, is given by the contract further wide powers by both employer and contractor, and in some matters he has an absolute discretion. In these matters he must act independently and without bias. As a consequence of this special position of his agent, the employer must not obstruct or interfere with the issue of a certificate and must give all fresh instructions to his agent. A certificate is the formal expression of a judgement, valuation or decision by a professional adviser, set forth in the terms prescribed in the contract conditions. Should orders be given by the employer direct to the contractor they would not be strictly admissible as variations under the existing contract, and could be held by the contractors to constitute either a fresh contract or an implied promise to pay reasonable remuneration.

[1] See Chapter 2, pp. 33–4.

Engineer's Responsibilities and Duties

The engineer referred to throughout the I.C.E. contract will usually be a civil engineer appointed by the employer to design and supervise the works and act as the employer's agent. The efficiency of the engineer and ultimately the success of the contract will be influenced by the quality of the employer's instructions. It is the engineer's responsibility and duty to do all within his power to ensure that the instructions received describe his client's requirements in sufficient detail to enable the design and supervision of the works to be performed effectively, and this cannot be achieved without the willing co-operation of the client. The importance of this co-operation increases with the size and power of the employer's organization. To aid the employer, the engineer should prepare a comprehensive list of possible requirements at the commencement of the preliminary negotiations, so that those mutual reproaches of "I was never told" and "You did not ask" do not cloud the relationship of client and consulting engineer during the later stages of the contract. One example of these misunderstandings occurred when an engineer designed and specified pre-cast pre-stressed concrete beams for a factory floor. It was a most economical design in all respects. Unfortunately the client was unappreciative, as his major requirement was a slab through which holes could be cut at short notice without diminishing the overall strength of the floor. A useful skill for the engineer is the ability to anticipate intelligently his client's possible requirements. A lively interest in the latest developments affecting the functions and processes that will be utilized will help in this respect.

With the larger corporations, and local authorities, the engineer may find himself acting as conciliator and co-ordinator between the different departments of the industrial concern, and between the local authority and the various ministries, one group being concerned with cost, another with function, and a third with appearance. These additional duties which do not come within the scope of his terms of engagement may impose a heavy burden on the engineer. In such cases the client in his own interest should be persuaded to nominate one departmental head to take the responsibility for all coordination. This will never be an easy matter, and when accepting a fresh appointment the engineer should endeavour to show the client the extent of the harm which could result from a faulty system of liaison and communication. The execution of the work is bound to be handicapped if the responsibility for detailed decisions is in the control of a committee.

Direct Labour

Both local authorities and large industrial concerns sometimes create direct labour forces to carry out maintenance, and occasionally employ them for new works. Mention should be made of the contractual status of such work, though this is not the place to discuss the merits or demerits of this system. As it is not possible to contract with oneself, no contract can be formed between a direct labour department and its parent organization; and the usual contract procedures must be adapted to satisfy the requirements that arise when the roles of employer and contractor are combined.

Contractors

The vast majority of all constructional work is carried out by contractors. Apart from a proportion of contractors which will be partnerships (firms) or one-man businesses, carrying out small works these will be companies with limited liability. In the case of contracts of a great magnitude, this company may be a consortium or a syndicate of contracting firms who have formed a temporary alliance for the purpose of tendering for and carrying out a single undertaking, or several of a like nature.

The contractor undertakes to construct or perform the works for a sum of money, which may be fixed or adjustable, in accordance with the engineer's instructions, and under his supervision, usually within a stated period of time. In addition to complying with the engineer's instructions the contractor must carry out the works in conformity with the law of the country in which he contracts, and any local regulations and by-laws; and must give all notices and pay all fees arising from these laws and regulations. Failure to do so will make the contractor liable for all penalties and additional costs of alterations arising from the breach of these laws. The accounts for such fees will be included in the interim valuations, and when reckoning the final cost of the contract. Should the regulations necessitate alterations to the engineer's design and details, the contractor should apply to the engineer for directions, for it is sometimes possible for the engineer to negotiate with the authority administering the regulations and obtain approval of his original design, and an agreement not to enforce a particular by-law. If the engineer takes upon himself the responsibility of serving notices, and fails to follow the correct procedure, the contractor can claim recompense for any penalties, and the additional costs of alterations incurred, from the employer, who could seek redress from the engineer.

Sub-contractors

Besides being responsible to the employer for the correctness of his own work, the contractor is liable also for the work of his sub-contractors, and, in general, for any defects in the materials or goods supplied by merchants and manufacturers. Unless excluded by the terms of the contract or the circumstance of the case, the law will imply into the contract between the employer and the contractor warranties on the part of the contractor that these materials will be of good quality and reasonably fit for the purpose for which they are required.[1] If the employer, or the architect or engineer on his behalf has chosen a particular material or brand of material the warranty of fitness for purpose

[1] *Young and Marten Ltd.* v. *McManus Childs Ltd.* [1969] 1 A.C. 454. 9 B.L.R. 77.

will be excluded. However, as long as the contractor has had an opportunity to agree the terms upon which he purchases the specified materials there will be implied a warranty of quality.[1] Both the implied warranties may be excluded if the employer denies the contractor opportunity to make reasonable objection to a particular supplier being nominated or to seek indemnity from the supplier.[1] This would occur, for example, where the employer has negotiated all of the terms of the proposed sub-contract with the sub-contractor or supplier and merely instructs the contractor to enter into a contract on those terms, without any opportunity to protect himself by taking express warranties from the supplier. The contractor's liability for the work of sub-contractors arises irrespective of whether the sub-contractor was nominated or of the contractors own choosing. The wording of the clauses found in the standard forms of contract, however, relating to these obligations differentiates between sub-contractors of the contractor's own choosing and those nominated by the engineer. It is important that the contractor imposes the same obligations upon the sub-contractors as are undertaken by himself, and he cannot be compelled by the employer to enter into a sub-contract with a nominated sub-contractor or supplier who declines to accept these conditions. Both the J.C.T. and I.C.E. standard forms of contract also provide that no nominated sub-contractor against whom the contractor makes reasonable objection need be employed. Standard forms of sub-contract for use in conjunction with the I.C.E. contract and J.C.T. contracts are available.

In the past the carrying out of civil engineering or building works has not involved any contract between employer and sub-contractor. This meant that redress for the failure of the sub-contractor to fulfil his obligations had to be obtained by the employer against the main contractor, who alone had the power to enforce the sub-contract or claim damages for the breach of it. However, in 1982 the House of Lords held that where a sub-contractor was nominated, the relationship between the employer and the sub-contractor could be so close as to fall only

[1] *Gloucestershire County Council* v. *Richardson* [1969] 1 A.C. 480. 9 B.L.R. 84. See also *Norta* v. *John Sisk* (1977) 14 B.L.R. 49.

just short of a contractual relationship, and that this proximity could make the sub-contractor liable to the employer under the ordinary principles of negligence[1]. Thus the employer may have a remedy against the sub-contractor despite the absence of a direct contract between them.

Prior to 1982, and in an attempt to give the employer a contractual right against the sub-contractor, a new standard form of collateral between employer and nominated sub-contractor was introduced in 1971 for use when the main contract is in J.C.T. form. This form now constitutes one of the appendices to the standard form of tender to be used by nominated sub-contractors where the main contract is a J.C.T. contract. By the collateral contract the sub-contractor, in consideration of (among other things) being nominated by the employer, gives warranties to the employer in respect of the design of the sub-contract works and the quality of the materials used in them and in respect of any performance specification included in his tender. He also warrants that he will carry out the sub-contract works in accordance with programme and supply the architect and the contractor with information so as to avoid delays. These warranties can be enforced by the employer directly against the sub-contractor. It should be emphasized that this collateral contract is additional to, and not in any way in substitution for, either the main contract between the employer and the contractor, or the sub-contract between the contractor and the sub-contractor. In many cases the collateral contract will not be used, either because it is inappropriate or because the sub-contractor declines to enter into it. In all such cases the traditional legal relationship will continue to apply unaltered. There is no comparable form of collateral contract for use with the I.C.E. contract.

Public works contractors will normally employ qualified civil engineers in key positions even when the financial control of the organization is in less specialized hands. The civil engineer who is engaged in contracting, besides undertaking the duties of design, supervision and direction, like his counterpart in

[1] *Junior Books* v. *Veitchi* [1982] 3 W.L.R. 477.

consulting engineering or the public service, must also be responsible for the planning, construction and profitability of the works. It would be unusual for him to combine the role of designer and constructor, though he may be called upon to act in each capacity at different times.

Communication between employer and contractor is likely therefore to be through the medium of two civil engineers, one being the spokesman of the firm constructing the work, and the other being a consultant acting as the employer's agent. The consultant, while carrying out his duties as the employer's agent, must also act impartially, and in a quasi-judicial capacity on many occasions. To discover when the consultant must act as the guardian of his employer's interests, and when he must act as the impartial certifier who determines the liabilities and obligations of both parties, can only be properly ascertained by looking at the clauses of the contract which deal with the relevant situations. As guardian, the engineer will find he will be called upon to use his technical skill and judgement; as certifier, he will need to exercise his impartiality as well as technical skill and judgement. Should the contractor or employer wish to dispute any decision of the engineer, either of them may, after the completion of the contract, refer the matter to an independent arbitrator, although disputes about the withholding of a certificate or retention money can be referred to an arbitrator while the contract is still in progress. A certifier has been defined as a preventer of disputes, and an arbitrator as a settler of disputes.

Negligence

An engineer as a professional, owes duties of care to those who may be affected by his acts. If he acts negligently he may be sued by his client for negligence or breach of the terms of his appointment. The scope of the law of negligence is constantly being widened by the courts, although there may be situations where on the facts the terms of the engineers contract may be held to limit his separate liability in tort.[1] There is no

---

[1] *William Hill Organisation* v. *Bernard Sunley and Sons* (1982) 22 B.L.R. 1.

contractual relationship between the engineer and the contractor, so that any extra cost incurred by the contractor as a result of the failure of the engineer to fulfil his duties and supply instructions and drawings at the correct time, is the liability of the employer. The employer can sue the engineer for this failure should he wish, provided that he can prove negligence.

If an engineer acts negligently he will be liable not only to his client but to anyone injured as a result of his negligence if he ought reasonably to have foreseen that they would be affected by his acts. In one case, for example, in which a workman was injured by the collapse of an obviously unsafe wall on a building site, the architect was held liable for the workman's injuries, as were the man's employers (who were building contractors) and the demolition contractors (who had advised the architect that the wall was safe).[1] On the other hand an architect has been held to have neither the duty nor the right to instruct the contractor as to the manner of execution of the works.[2] A professional who gives guidance or advice to others owes a duty of care not only to his client but to anyone else who he knows will rely on his skill and judgement.[3] Hence he may be liable for his negligence in, for example, approving inadequate foundations, to a subsequent purchaser of the structure built on such foundations.[4]

However, neither the employer nor anyone else can demand perfection. The duty of an architect or engineer is to use reasonable skill and care. He does not guarantee perfection, and, in the absence of special circumstances or an express or implied warranty to the employer, he does not promise that his efforts will achieve the desired result.[5] The standard of care and skill of an engineer is that of ordinary professional competence, measured by the state of the art and the standards of the time when his work was carried out. In most professions the general

[1] *Clay* v. *A. J. Crump* [1964] 1 Q.B. 533.

[2] *Oldschool* v. *Gleeson Construction Ltd.* (1976) 4 B.L.R. 103.

[3] See, e.g., *Yianni* v. *Edwin Evans and Sons* [1981] 3 All E.R. 592 and *J.E.B. Fasteners* v. *Marks, Bloom & Co.* [1983] 1 All E.R. 583.

[4] *Dutton* v. *Bognor Regis Building Co. Ltd.* [1972] 1 Q.B. 373.

[5] *Greaves & Co. (Contractors) Ltd.* v. *Baynham Meikle and Partners* [1975] 1 W.L.R. 1095.

trend is for the standard to be progressively raised as time passes. This would result in a gradual imposition of an intolerable burden on the consulting engineer as the demands became more exacting and complex. Fortunately, the stress is reduced by sharing among an increased number of specialists the tasks that at one time would have been borne by an individual. Today the success of an engineer may depend partly on his ability to supervise, direct and coordinate the work of a team of specialists. Specialization is usual in one or several allied classes of work, combined with an outline knowledge of much else.

The law, however, does not permit an architect or engineer to delegate to others his responsibility for design unless such delegation is expressly authorized within his contract or by his client. In one case a building failed after only two years because of the defective design of its reinforced concrete frame. The owner sued the architect for damages. The architect pleaded that he had implied authority to delegate responsibility for parts of the design of the building and had delegated his responsibility for the concrete frame to the contractor. The court held that in the absence of an express authority there was no implied authority to delegate design, especially to the contractor. The architect owes his design duties to the employer, whose interests so often clash with those of the contractor.[1]

The question whether an engineer or architect could be liable to his client for negligent certification has been the subject of much uncertainty in the past. The question has now been authoritatively answered, however, by a judicial decision of the House of Lords. In general an engineer or architect will be liable to his client for negligence in certifying the value of work under a civil engineering or building contract. But an engineer or architect appointed to act as an arbitrator, or to settle some specific dispute between the parties to a civil engineering or building contract (as opposed to the general function of certifying the value of work thereunder), is in a different position and will not be liable for his negligence.[2]

---

[1] *Moresk Cleaners Ltd.* v. *Hicks* (1966) 4 B.L.R. 50.

[2] *Sutcliffe* v. *Thackrah* [1974] A.C. 727.

The liability of an engineer for negligent design and supervision may last for many more years than his contractual liabilities. An action for damages for breach of contract must be brought within six years of the date of the breach, or twelve years if the contract is under seal.[1] In negligence, however, the action may be brought within six years of the accrual of the cause of action.[2] In the case of latent defects in a building or other structure it has now been held by the House of Lords that the cause of action does not accrue until actual physical damage to the structure occurs.[3] Thus, when cracking first occurs in a structure as a result of negligence in its design some twenty years earlier it is too late to sue for breach of contract, but the six year limit in tort is only just beginning and the designer will not be able to hide behind the protection of the Limitation Act until it expires some twenty-six years after the negligence complained of! An exception to this rule appears to be where the negligence is such that the building is doomed from the start[4], though it is difficult to understand how such a building can be anything but doomed from the start if it subsequently suffers damage caused by bad design. In that situation the six year period begins running when the negligence occurs, irrespective of whether actual damage has occurred. It should be noted that as a result of this decision of the House of Lords it is immaterial that the damage is not reasonably discoverable. As long as the damage has occurred time begins to run even if nobody is aware of it. It is suggested that this is likely to cause great problems for those charged with the task of advising on the date of occurrence of damage, and that a change in the law to clarify the situation is well overdue.

Consultants

The other consultants who may assist the engineer include heating and ventilating engineers, mechanical and electrical

---

[1] Limitation Act, 1980 sections 5 and 8.

[2] Ibid section 2.

[3] *Pirelli General Cable Works Ltd.* v. *Oscar Faber & Partners* [1983] 2 W.L.R. 6.

[4] Ibid., p. 14.

engineers, architects and quantity surveyors. They will be required to accept the overriding authority of the engineer, but it is customary for them to have a separate agreement with the employer. The services of architects on civil engineering contracts are generally required for landscaping and the design of subsidiary buildings. Building contracts are mostly supervised by architects; it is the structural engineer who will assist as consultant responsible for the design and inspection of the foundations and structure; and the J.C.T. Quantities Contract will be used.

Resident Engineers

A resident engineer will be required on large contracts. He is the engineer's representative and has a wide variety of duties. Occasionally he is an assistant of the engineer who has had some part in the design and preparation of the contract drawings. Either the engineer or the employer can appoint him, and sometimes government departments and local authorities stipulate that the resident engineer should be a member of their permanent staff, possibly a man specializing in site inspection. The engineer cannot avoid personal liability by blaming the negligence or incompetence of this representative, whether he be an assistant from the engineer's office or a resident appointed by the employers.[1] This responsibility remains even when an employer nominates a representative to whom the engineer objects. The resident engineer's duties are primarily to inspect the works, and test and examine the materials. In addition he may receive delegated power to give written instructions amplifying and varying the works. Sometimes these delegated powers will be very wide. Nevertheless, should the contractor be dissatisfied with any decision of the engineer's

---

[1] A resident engineer appointed by the employer with the engineer's approval, and paid by the employer, is an employee of the employer: *Morren* v. *Swinton and Pendlebury Borough Council* [1965] 2 All E.R. 349. In these circumstances negligent acts towards third parties by the resident engineer may also render the employer vicariously liable.

representative, he can always appeal to the engineer. Similarly, the engineer retains the power to condemn bad work which this representative, for one reason or another, failed to disapprove. Therefore, an important quality in any resident engineer is his talent for reflecting in his actions and his decisions the outlook of his principal, while at the same time exercising his own initiative when called for.

The drawings and specification may have been prepared with the greatest care, yet it is inevitable that in the day to day performance of the works alterations will be called for, and decisions required.[1] The smooth running of the contract will depend on the ability of the resident engineer to answer the contractor's queries promptly. His success will, in part, depend on the support he receives from the consultant's office; but he can anticipate trouble by carefully checking the drawings in detail for errors and omissions before they are used on the site. In carrying out his duties, tact, diplomacy and geniality will be needed; and he should always try to be available when the contractor needs him for inspecting sections of the work, or answering queries.

A resident engineer should always keep a diary in which a daily record is made of the number of men employed, the progress of the work, instructions given or transmitted, the arrival and departure of mechanical plant, stoppages, the state of the weather, particulars of visitors to the site, and anything else he should consider relevant. These records can be of great value later. The contract lays down a procedure for the notification in writing of instructions affecting the value of the contract. In practice this routine is not always adhered to. Memories grow dim and conflicting. Properly kept, the diary can help to resolve disputes later. The busiest days will call for the longest entries, so the keeping of the record must be made an unfailing routine. For the diary will immediately lose much value if it is kept intermittently or is only written up weekly.

Clerks of works are employed as inspectors of works on building contracts, sometimes in conjunction with a resident

[1] See p. 203.

engineer. When the engineer's representative only visits the site periodically, he will depend on the clerk of works for much of the site inspection. Sometimes the resident engineer will be assisted by inspectors of works and by assistant engineers.

Agent

When the I.C.E. contract is used, the contractor must place in charge of the works a competent agent or representative who has received the written approval of the engineer. This agent will usually be a qualified civil engineer responsible for the organization and supervision on the contractor's behalf, often functioning independently of his head office, apart from guidance given at the commencement on general policy. A general foreman will normally be in charge of all labour. Assisting the agent will be a staff of assistant engineers, measuring surveyors and clerical staff employed by the contractor. The agent will frequently be senior in age and experience to the resident engineer and his freedom of action will depend both on his own capabilities and the organization of his firm. The J.C.T. quantities contract for building works imposes upon the contractor the duty to keep constantly upon the works a competent foreman-in-charge. This man will usually be a general foreman who received his initial training as craftsman in one of the building trades, and progressed through the lower grades of foremanship to a general foremanship. It is extremely unlikely that he would be given powers analogous to that of the civil engineering agent. His responsibilities will vary with the size of the contract and the policy of his company. Usually he will be concerned solely with the day to day running of the job, but he should also be given the opportunity to express his often pungent and practical opinions on the management's policy. Programme planning and decision on policy will be undertaken by a contracts manager. It is not unknown for building contractors to place an agent in charge of large scale building projects, and this practice is gradually being more widely adopted.

Quantity Surveyors

Quantity surveyors either in private practice, or in the public service, are almost invariably employed on building contracts. Their duties extend from preparing preliminary estimates from the sketch designs to the preparation of the final account, and will include, among other services, the preparation of the bills of quantities, and valuations for interim certificates. The quantity surveyor receives official recognition and his duties are partially defined in the J.C.T. quantities form. The I.C.E. form does not mention by name the quantity surveyor, but the engineer can, if he wishes, delegate his duties in regard to measurement and valuation to a quantity surveyor but not in regard to the final certificate. Some civil engineers still prepare their own quantities, but with the increasing complexity of engineering schemes, many civil engineers now employ the services of the professional quantity surveyor.

For many years quantity surveyors, either in private practice or in government service, have been employed to prepare bills of quantities and settle final accounts for engineering works undertaken by government departments.

Co-operation

The work and responsibilities of these and other participants in the construction industries will be dealt with more fully when particular aspects of a contract are explained in the following chapters. From what has already been written it will be seen that the success of any one of them will be dependent on the actions of the others. A willingness to co-operate, and a sympathetic understanding of the problems of the other participants, will always be vital to the achievement of optimum efficiency.

CHAPTER 2

LEGAL ASPECTS OF CONTRACTS

The Formation of a Contract

This chapter deals with the general principles of English law relating to the formation of contracts. The legal aspects of the carrying out of civil engineering contracts are dealt with in later chapters under the appropriate subject-headings.

Several Acts of Parliament affect civil engineering contracts. In general, however, the making of civil engineering contracts is governed by the ordinary rules of the English law of contract and is not regulated by any code laid down by statute. The law of contract is largely common law; it consists in the main of rules evolved from judicial decisions rather than rules made by legislation.

Civil engineering contracts are usually made in writing in one of the standard forms dealt with in Chapter 3. These forms have many advantages and their use is to to be desired. It is important to remember, however, that in general the making of a contract requires no formality. A binding contract may be made as well by an exchange of letters as by the parties signing an elaborate printed document. Subject to certain exceptions, dealt with below, a binding contract may equally well be made by word of mouth. There is no legal reason, although there are many practical ones, why a civil engineering contract should not be made orally.

Employers, consultants or contractors are unlikely to choose to make a civil engineering contract for a large project orally, or by exchange of letters. It is not wholly unknown, however, for contracts involving large sums of money to be made in one of these ways by inadvertence. The making of small sub-contracts by letter or by word of mouth is perhaps more common.

Offer and Acceptance

The Offer

The basis of contract is agreement. Agreement is composed of an offer and an acceptance. In order to see whether a contract has been made the law looks to see whether one party has made an offer to do or refrain from doing something, and, if so, whether that offer has been accepted by the other party. The test which the law applies is an objective one: it looks at the parties' conduct, not their intentions. If one party makes a firm offer which is unequivocally accepted by the other, neither can afterwards contend that he did not intend to enter into a contract.[1]

An offer, however, must be distinguished from a mere attempt to negotiate. The latter is called by lawyers "an invitation to treat". An offer, if accepted, becomes a binding contract. An invitation to treat, on the other hand, is something which by its nature is incapable of being accepted or becoming binding without further negotiation.

An invitation to tender sent by an employer to a number of contractors is generally an invitation to treat rather than an offer[2], although it may be that by inserting words to the effect that the lowest tender will be accepted it might be turned into an offer capable of acceptance. It follows that the clause frequently inserted to the effect that the employer does not bind himself to accept the lowest or any tender is probably unnecessary.

A document or something said by one of the parties may constitute an offer although the party putting it forward does not use the word "offer". "Estimates" have frequently been

[1] *Falck* v. *Williams* [1900] A.C. 176.

[2] *Moore* v. *Shawcross* [1954] C.L.Y. 342.

held to be offers which become binding when accepted.[1] Whether or not a civil engineering contractor's tender is an offer depends upon its terms. The object of making a tender is, of course, to communicate a firm offer to the employer. If the contractor's offer is definite and unambiguous in its terms it will constitute an offer unless it contains words to the contrary.

But care must be taken where the tender is one made by a prospective nominated sub-contractor to the architect. It has been held that the architect is not the agent of the main contractor for the purpose of making contracts, and that accordingly the main contractor's order to the sub-contractor is not an acceptance of an offer made to him, but merely an offer or counter-offer. There is no binding contract until the sub-contractor accepts the order by performance or otherwise.[2]

Frequently, however, a tender will contain the words "subject to contract" or some similar words which indicate that something more has to be done before a binding contract can be made by acceptance of the terms of the tender. The effect of the words "subject to contract" is considered below.

At the time when the contractor makes his tender no contract is in existence. The cost of preparing the tender therefore falls upon the contractor, unless he can show that the employer fraudulently invited the tender without ever intending to accept it or to consider it, in which case he may have a claim for damages against the employer.[3]

An offer may be revoked by the person who makes it at any time before it is accepted. The revocation takes effect, however, from the time when it comes to the notice of the person to whom the offer was made and not from the time when the maker of the offer decides to revoke.[4] If the contractor accepts the offer before he he has knowledge of it's revocation but in the meantime the employer has let the contract to

---

[1] *Croshaw* v. *Pritchard* (1899) 16 T.L.R. 45 and also *Cana Construction* v. *The Queen* (1973) 37 D.L.R. (3d) 418.

[2] *A. Davies & Co. (Shopfitters) Ltd.* v. *William Old Ltd.* (1969) 67 L.G.R. 395.

[3] *Richardson* v. *Silvester* (1873) L.R. 9 Q.B. 34.

[4] *Byrne* v. *Van Tienhoven* (1880) 5 C.P.D. 344.

another contractor, the contractor will be entitled to damages for breach of contract. If the notice of revocation is sent by post it takes effect from the time of receipt, not the time of posting. It is important therefore for an employer or contractor who wishes to revoke an offer to communicate his intention to the other party without delay. Notice of revocation, however, need not necessarily be given by the person who himself makes the offer; it is sufficient notice of revocation if the person to whom the offer was made learns of the revocation from a third party.[1]

A notice of revocation, if it is to be effective, must be in clear terms that permit of no doubt as to its meaning. An equivocal letter is not a valid notice of revocation.[2]

An offer that is not revoked does not remain open indefinitely. If it is not accepted within a reasonable time it is deemed to lapse and cannot afterwards be accepted.[3] There is no general rule defining the length of a "reasonable time". What is a reasonable time has to be ascertained in each case from all the circumstances.

The general rules about revocation of offers, described in the preceding two paragraphs, can be abrogated by the parties if they so wish. They can stipulate, if they choose, that an offer should remain open for a prescribed period of time or, indeed, that it should remain open indefinitely. These stipulations, however, if they are to have binding effect, must form the subject of a contract – a preliminary contract to the principal contract contemplated by the parties – which is itself governed by the rules described in this chapter.

In addition to revocation and lapse of time, an offer may also be terminated by the occurrence of a stipulated or implied condition, or by the death of one of the parties, but this will always be a matter of construction depending on the terms and wording of the offer.

---

[1] *Dickinson* v. *Dodds* [1876] Ch. 2 D. 463.

[2] *Peter Lind & Co. Ltd.* v. *Mersey Docks & Harbour Board* [1972] 2 Lloyd's Rep. 234.

[3] *Ramsgate Hotel Co.* v. *Montefiore* (1866) L.R. 1 Ex. 109.

The Acceptance

The acceptance of an offer must be unconditional and it must be communicated to the person who makes the offer. In order to be unconditional the terms of the acceptance must correspond precisely with the terms of the offer. This does not mean that the acceptance need set out all the words used in the offer: the words "I accept your offer" constitute an unconditional acceptance. But if the person to whom the offer is made introduces into a purported acceptance some new term that is either contrary to a term of the offer or that is not contained in the offer, the acceptance is not unconditional and does not bring a binding contract into existence. Thus an offer to pay a fixed price to a contractor cannot be accepted by the contractors promise to do the work for a fluctuating price.[1] A purported acceptance of this kind, however, may amount to a fresh offer by the person to whom the original offer was made.

The effect of a counter-offer made in this way is to destroy the original offer.[2] The counter-offer is subject to the same rules about acceptance as the original offer. Thus in one case a building contractor purported to accept an offer from a specialist sub-contractor in a letter which sought to incorporate the main contractor's standard printed conditions of contract. As these conditions formed no part of the sub-contractor's original offer, the purported acceptance was held by the court to be a counter-offer, and there was therefore no binding contract until that counter-offer had been accepted by the sub-contractor.[3]

In practice, of course, parties negotiating a bargain may, during the course of the negotiations, make or demand numerous concessions about the price of the works and other terms. Offer may be met by counter-offer, counter-offer by a further counter-offer from the original offerer, and so on through a series of counter-offers until agreement is reached

[1] *N.W. Leics D.C.* v. *East Midlands Ltd.* [1981] 1 W.L.R. 1396.

[2] *Hyde* v. *Wrench* (1840) 3 Beav. 334.

[3] *A. Davies & Co. (Shopfitters) Ltd.* v. *William Old Ltd.* (1969) 67 L.G.R. 395.

and one or other of the parties makes an unconditional acceptance. Contracts concluded in this way raise many practical difficulties. The terms of the contract, instead of being contained in one document, may be scattered through a thick file of correspondence, or may be contained partly in letters, partly in telephone messages and partly in unrecorded conversations. In these circumstances it is sometimes difficult to ascertain precisely what has been agreed and when the agreement came into being.

For this reason an offer or acceptance is often expressed as being "subject to contract", "subject to formal contract" or "subject to a proper contract being drawn up". These expressions can have one or other of two meanings. They may mean either that it is a condition of the bargain that a formal document should be drawn up, or that the drawing up of a formal document should merely be one of the means of carrying out a transaction already agreed.[1] In the former case no binding contract comes into existence until the formal document is drawn up and agreed. In the latter case a binding contract is in existence whether or not a formal document is drawn up or agreed. Which of the two meanings is the more appropriate in any particular case has to be decided by reference to the surrounding circumstances. In practice, however, the courts tend to hold that an agreement made "subject to contract" is of no legal effect until a formal contract is agreed, unless there is very strong evidence in support of the contrary view.

An acceptance must be clear and unambiguous in its terms. In a case building contractors were asked by employers to submit two tenders for the construction of a container freight terminal, the first at a fixed price and the second at a price varying with the cost of labour and materials. The contractors submitted the two tenders as requested, and it was agreed that the tenders should be kept open for six months. Immediately before the expiry of the six months the employers wrote to the contractors stating that they accepted "your tender". In the circumstances there was no clear indication whether it was the

---

[1] *Hatzfeldt-Wildenburg* v. *Alexander* [1912] 1 Ch. 284, at pp. 288–9.

fixed price tender or the variable price tender which was being accepted, and the court held that the letter did not constitute an acceptance and that there was no binding contract.[1]

Communication of the Acceptance

Acceptance of an offer, if it is to create a binding contract, must be communicated to the person who makes the offer. The method of communicating the acceptance may be stipulated in the offer; the person who makes the offer may stipulate, for example, that acceptance may only be made in writing on a particular form. If this is the case no binding contract comes into being until acceptance is made in the way prescribed.

More often than not, however, no particular method of acceptance is prescribed by the person making the offer. In these circumstances it is presumed that the acceptance may be communicated in the same way as the offer; if the offer is sent by post, for example, the acceptance may also be sent by post.

The general rule is that the risk of the communication of the acceptance not reaching the person who makes the offer is borne by the person to whom the offer is made. If for some reason, perhaps beyond the control of the parties, the communication of the acceptance fails to reach the person for whom it is intended, no binding contract comes into existence. If, for instance, the acceptance is communicated by telephone and the line goes dead, or is so indistinct that the acceptance cannot be heard, no contract is made.[2] The contract is made when the acceptance is communicated, and accordingly it is deemed to have been made at the place where the acceptance is received. The same principle has been applied by the courts to Telex communications.[3]

There are two important exceptions to this general rule. The

---

[1] *Peter Lind & Co. Ltd.* v. *Mersey Docks & Harbour Board* [1972] 2 Lloyd's Rep. 234.

[2] *Entores* v. *Miles Far East Corporation* [1955] 2 Q.B. 327, at pp. 332–3.

[3] Ibid., p. 333. *See also Brinkibon Ltd.* v. *Stahag Stahl und Stahlwaren-handel-gesellschaft Gmbh* [1980] 2 Lloyd's Rep. 556.

exceptions are acceptances communicated by post or telegram. In these cases the rule is that the acceptance is complete from the moment that the letter is posted or the telegram handed in.[1] It should be noted, therefore, that if letters cross in the post accepting the offer on the one hand and revoking it on the other, a binding contract is made, because the acceptance is deemed to be complete before the revocation is deemed to be communicated.[2]

A person who makes an offer cannot validly make a stipulation that the silence of the person to whom he makes it will amount to an acceptance. A stipulation in these terms has no binding effect.[3] In certain circumstances, however, the conduct of a person may amount to acceptance of an offer. If an employer offers to employ a contractor to do specified works on specified terms for a specified price, and the contractor without further ado does the work, the contractor will be deemed to have accepted the employer's offer by his conduct, and will not afterwards be able to seek payment on different terms or of a higher price.[4]

"Battle of Forms"

Problems invariably arise where both parties purport to contract upon their own standard terms and conditions. Where an employer places an order which is expressed to be subject to his standard terms and conditions, and the contractor's acceptance is stated to be in accordance with his own terms and conditions of trading the contractor cannot be said to have accepted the order. It has been suggested that if the work is subsequently carried out then a contract must have been made and that the performance by both parties of their obligations is evidence that the contractor's counter-offer has been accepted.

[1] *Henthorn* v. *Fraser* [1892] 2 Ch. 27, 33.

[2] *Re London and Northern Bank, ex. p. Jones* [1900] 1 Ch. 220.

[3] *Felthouse* v. *Bindley* (1862) 11 C.B. [N.S.] 869; *Fairline Shipping Corporation* v. *Adamson* [1975] Q.B. 180.

[4] *Brogden* v. *Metropolitan Railway* [1877] 2 App. Cas. 666.

There is some support for this "last-shot" argument.[1] Each case must depend on its own particular facts, and the position appears to be as stated in 1979 by Lord Denning, M.R.;

> "In some cases the battle is won by the man who gets the blow in first. If he offers to sell at a named price on the terms and conditions stated on the back: and the buyer orders the goods purporting to accept the offer on an order form with his own terms and conditions on the back – then if the difference is so material that it would affect the price, the buyer might not be allowed to take advantage of the difference unless he draws it specifically to the attention of the seller. There are other cases where the battle depends on the shots fired on both sides. There is a concluded contract but the forms vary. The terms and conditions are to be construed together. If they can be reconciled so as to give a harmonious result, all well and good. If differences are irreconcilable – so that they are mutually contradictory – then the conflicting terms may have to be scrapped and replaced by a reasonable implication."[2]

Such uncertainty in a contract is clearly undesirable. It may be that standard terms on the back of orders, acceptances and acknowledgements can be drafted in such a way that they cancel out the other party's terms. That will prevent the other party winning the battle of the forms. But to draft terms which are guaranteed to prevail would be a difficult, if not impossible, task. The best that clever drafting can hope to obtain is that the terms of both parties are scrapped and that the contractor is paid a reasonable sum for his work.

Because of these difficulties it is clearly preferable to enter into a formal contract wherever possible so that there may be certainty as to the terms of the agreement.

---

[1] *B.R.S.* v. *Arthur Crutchley Ltd.* [1968] 1 A.E.R. 811.
[2] *Butler Machine Tool* v. *Ex-Cell-O Corpn.* [1979] 1 W.L.R. 401.

Certainty of Terms

In order to constitute a valid contract the parties must so express themselves that their meaning can be determined with a reasonable degree of certainty.[1] A purported offer and acceptance in which the terms of the proposed agreement are left so vague that it is impossible to determine what the parties agreed does not constitute a binding contract. This is not to say that the inclusion of a vague or meaningless term will necessarily invalidate the whole contract.

Provided that no essential term is omitted or left uncertain the contract will be binding.[2] The terms *essential*, however, to a contract relating to a civil engineering project are likely to be numerous. One term which is clearly essential to a building or civil engineering contract is the price or, at least, the means of ascertaining the price. In 1975 the Court of Appeal considered a case in which developers approached a building contractor to ask him to build a motel, a hotel, and a filling station which were to form a complex of buildings on the same site. The contractor asked that, if he arranged the necessary finance, the developers should undertake to instruct their quantity surveyor "to negotiate fair and reasonable contract sums in respect of each of the three projects as they arise ... based upon agreed estimates of the net cost of work and general overheads with a margin for profit of 5 per cent". The developers agreed to this proposition. The court held that there was no enforceable contract because there was no agreed price or agreed method of ascertaining the price without further negotiation between the parties.[3] In such a case the contractor will be paid a reasonable sum (*quantum meruit*). The pitfalls of omitting essential terms and of failure to secure precision are, in most circumstances, avoided by use of one of the standard forms of contract.

---

[1] *Scammell* v. *Ouston* [1941] A.C. 251, at p. 255.

[2] *Hillas & Co. Ltd.* v. *Arcos Ltd.* (1932) 38 Com. Cas. 23, at p. 43; *Nicolene Ltd.* v. *Simmonds* [1953] 1 Q.B. 543, at p. 552.

[3] *Courtney & Fairbairn Ltd.* v. *Tolaini Brothers (Hotels) Ltd.* [1975] 1 W.L.R. 297.

The terms of the contract need not be set out in full in the documents or the conversations which constitute the offer and acceptance. Terms contained in some other document, in a set of standard conditions, for instance, may be incorporated in the contract by reference.

In another case in 1975, for example, main contractors placed an order with sub-contractors for work to be carried out "... in full accordance with the appropriate form for nominated sub-contractors (R.I.B.A. 1965 edition)." The order was accepted. The Court of Appeal held that all the terms of the appropriate standard form of sub-contracts for use when the main contract is in the J.C.T. form were deemed to be incorporated in the sub-contract.[1] But subject to certain exceptions which are dealt with later in this chapter, a party cannot be bound by any terms which are not expressly referred to in the documents or conversations which constitute the contract, or in documents or conversations incorporated into the contract by reference. A party to a contract cannot afterwards enforce a term by saying "I intended this to be a term of the agreement", if his intention was not brought to the notice of the other party when the contract was made. Special conditions suggested by one party in letters exchanged during negotiations before the signing of a contract in standard form cannot afterwards be enforced unless they are incorporated in the contractual documents.[2]

Where appropriate the courts will accept evidence of trade customs and usage or a course of dealing between the parties in order to see whether, read in the light of these factors, the terms of the contract are sufficiently certain. But this will not always be the case.[3]

Conversely there are sometimes occasions when both parties to a contract intend that certain conditions should apply even when they have not been expressly referred to. In one case,

[1] *Modern Buildings Wales Ltd.* v. *Limmer and Trinidad Co. Ltd.* [1975] 1 W.L.R. 1281. See also *Brightside Kilpatrick Engineering Services* v. *Mitchell Construction* (1973) *Ltd.* [1975] 2 Lloyd's Rep. 493.

[2] *London County Council* v. *Henry Boot & Sons Ltd.* [1959] 1 W.L.R. 1069.

[3] *Salsi* v. *Jetspeed Air Services Ltd.* [1977] 2 Lloyd's Rep. 57.

for example, civil engineering contractors (who were themselves in the plant-hire business) urgently required the use of a dragline crane. Arrangements were made by telephone with another plant-hire firm for the hire of such a crane. Hiring and transport charges were agreed but nothing was said on the telephone about conditions of hire. Both parties knew, however, that there were standard conditions of hire which were habitually imposed when such cranes were let on hire and both parties knew the substance of these conditions. The court held that the conditions were incorporated in the contract of hire, even although they had not been expressly referred to.[1]

Consideration

Another essential to the formation of a binding contract, other than a contract under seal, is that the agreement must be supported by *consideration*. *Consideration* has been judicially defined: "An act of forbearance of one party, or the promise thereof, is the price for which the promise of the other is bought, and the promise thus given for value is enforceable."[2] In civil engineering contracts the consideration for the promise made by the contractor (i.e. his promise to carry out the works) will usually be the promise by the employer to pay the price. Forbearance to sue for some previous breach of contract is, however, equally good consideration.

A more complex situation occurs when more than two parties stand to gain or lose by the transaction. A contract may provide, for example, that the price shall be paid by the employer not to the contractor but to an associated company of the contractor. If the employer fails to pay the associated company the contractor has a right to sue the employer for breach of contract, for he has given consideration (i.e. his promise to do the work), but he has suffered no damage as he

[1] *British Crane Hire Corporation Ltd.* v. *Ipswich Plant Hire Ltd.* [1975] Q.B. 303.

[2] *Dunlop* v. *Selfridge* [1915] A.C. 847, at p. 855, and *The Golden Lake* [1982] 2 Lloyd's Rep. 632.

was not the one intended to be paid. He may only be entitled to nominal damages. The associated company, however, cannot enforce the contract against the employer because it has given no consideration for the promise made in its favour.

The law has no interest in the adequacy of the consideration given. If an employer or contractor makes a foolish bargain, which he afterwards regrets, the court will not relieve him from its consequences, however oppressive they may be.

Contracts Which Must be in Writing

A binding contract, as has been noted earlier in this chapter, need not be in formal language or writing. To this rule there are three relevant exceptions. First, a contract "to answer for the debt, default or miscarriage of another person", that is to say a contract of suretyship or guarantee, must be evidenced in writing. This is required by section 4 of the Statute of Frauds, 1677. The Statute of Frauds formerly affected contracts of a number of other kinds, but was partially repealed by the Law Reform (Enforcement of Contracts) Act, 1954. Its effect is now limited to contracts of suretyship and guarantee.

The second exception relates to contracts for the sale of land. Section 40 (1) of the Law of Property Act, 1925, provides that a contract for the sale or other disposition of land or any interest in land cannot be enforced unless it is in writing, or recorded in writing, and signed by the person disposing of the land or his agent. A civil engineering contract is not usually affected by this section, for it would be unusual for such a contract to contain an agreement for the sale or other disposition of land or any interest in land. The contractor invariably obtains under the terms of a civil engineering contract a right to occupy land belonging to the employer in order to carry out the contract works. This right to occupy land, however, amounts in law only to a *revocable licence*, and does not constitute a "disposition of land or any interest in land".[1]

[1] *Camden* v. *Batterbury* (1860) 7 C.B. (N.S.) 864.

The third exception is that contracts made with corporations before 29 July, 1960, had to be under seal. This rule has been abrogated by the Corporate Bodies' Contracts Act, 1960, in respect of contracts made with corporations since that date.

A contract in writing may be made under seal, or may be merely signed by the parties without being sealed. The latter is called a "simple contract". An important distinction between contracts under seal and simple contracts is that an action for breach of a contract under seal may be brought at any time up to 12 years after the date of the breach, whereas an action for breach of a simple contract must be brought within 6 years from the breach.

In recent years, however, greater emphasis has been placed upon the law of negligence in which a different limitation period may apply, as discussed in Chapter 1.[1]

The Parties to a Contract

Corporations

In describing the rules which govern the formation of a contract the contracting parties are referred to in this chapter, for the sake of simplicity, as if they were individual persons. In practice, of course, the parties to civil engineering contracts are likely to be corporations, or, from time to time, unincorporated groups of persons.

Corporations can be classified in a number of ways. They are divided into corporations sole and corporations aggregate. A corporation sole consists of a single person and his successors in office. The Crown, the Archbishop of Canterbury, the Treasury Solicitor and the Public Trustee are all examples of the corporation sole. A corporation aggregate is composed of a group of individuals, but has an identity in law separate and distinct from the identities of its members. A corporation is therefore sometimes referred to by lawyers as a *legal person*.

[1] Limitation Act, 1980 (c.58).

The commonest example of a corporation aggregate is a company with limited liability incorporated under the provisions of the Companies Acts. Local authorities are also examples of corporations aggregate.

A corporation created by statute, or the proceedings of which are regulated by statute, does not have the same freedom to make contracts as that possessed by an individual. The power to contract of such a corporation, whether sole or aggregate, is limited by the statute under which it is created or which regulates its proceedings. Powers may be expressly conferred by a statute, or may be reasonably inferred from its terms.

Formerly the general rule was that if a corporation purported to make a contract which was beyond these powers the contract was *ultra vires* (that is to say beyond its powers) and therefore void.[1] This rule has been substantially modified, however, by the European Communities Act, 1972, Section 9, which came into force on 1 January 1973. Since that date any transaction decided on by the directors of a company is deemed, in favour of a person dealing with a company in good faith, to be one which it is within the company's capacity to enter into, and the directors' power to bind the company is deemed to be free of any limitation under the Memorandum or Articles of Association. A party to a transaction so decided on is not bound to enquire as to the company's capacity to enter into it or as to any such limitation on the directors' powers, and will be presumed to have acted in good faith unless the contrary is proved. As regards a person dealing with a company in good faith, therefore, the doctrine of *ultra vires* has been abolished. It remains, however, in relation to persons dealing with a company in bad faith and to the accountability of the directors for their acts to their own company.

Local Authorities

The contracts made by a local authority must accord with its standing orders. Standing orders made by a local authority with

[1] *Ashbury Railway Carriage and Iron Co.* v. *Riche* [1875] L.R. 7 H.L. 653.

respect to contracts for the supply of goods or materials or for the execution of works must include provision for securing competition for such contracts and for regulating the manner in which tenders are invited, but may exempt from any such provision contracts for a price below that specified in the standing orders, and may authorize the local authority to except any contract from any such provision when the authority is satisfied that the exception is justified by special circumstances.[1] A person dealing with a local authority, however, does not have to make enquiries to see that the standing orders have been complied with. A contract made by a local authority has binding effect notwithstanding that it is not in accordance with one or more of the standing orders.[2]

Unincorporated Associations

An unincorporated association, such as a members' club, is not a *legal person*. It is merely a name collectively applied to a group of individuals. An unincorporated association, with the exceptions of trade unions and unincorporated employers' associations, cannot therefore either sue or be sued. This is not to say that a valid contract cannot be made with the members of an unincorporated association. The members of an unincorporated members' club, for example, are liable upon a contract entered into by the trustees or committee of management of the club, provided that the making of the contract is within the scope of the authority given to the trustees, or the committee of management of the club, as the case may be, by the rules of the club; or, if the making of the contract is beyond that authority, provided that it is expressly sanctioned or subsequently ratified by the members.[3] The Rules of the English Supreme Court (i.e. the High Court and the Court of Appeal) make provision for representative actions to be brought, in which a small number of persons are authorized to bring or defend an action on behalf

[1] Local Government Act, 1972.
[1] Local Government Act, 1972.
[3] *Steele* v. *Gourley* (1887) 3 T.L.R. 772.

of a greater number, where otherwise a large number of members would have to be joined as parties to an action.[1]

Trade Unions and Employers' Associations

A trade union or an unincorporated employers' association can sue, or be sued upon a civil engineering contract made with it,[2] even although it is not a corporation; damages awarded against a registered trade union for breach of such a contract are recoverable only from the union's funds or property held in trust for it[3] and not from individual members.

Construing Contracts

The first aim in drafting a civil engineering or any other contract must be to achieve precision of language. Brevity, simplicity and elegance are all desirable virtues of style, but must remain subsidiary to the virtue of being clear and precise. The standard forms of civil engineering contract are not perhaps the most elegantly written or easily readable documents in the English language but they have the merit of defining with some precision the rights and duties of the contracting parties.

The reason for the lawyers' insistence upon precision in the drafting of contracts is the rule that the courts determine the intentions of the parties by looking at the words they have used in their contract, and not by listening to evidence of what the parties had in their minds, or their motives or purposes. "One must consider the meaning of the words used, not what one may guess to be the intention of the parties."[4] Much time and money can be spent upon deciding the meaning of words which are

[1] R.S.C., Order 15, rule 12.
[2] Trade Union and Labour Relations Act, 1974.
[3] *Bonsor* v. *Musicians' Union* [1956] A.C. 104.
[4] *Smith* v. *Lucas* (1881) 18 Ch. D. 531, at p. 542, *per* Jessel M.R.

unclear or ambiguous, or upon the application of general words in a contract to a particular situation to which the parties have not sufficiently applied their minds.

Rules of Construction

The courts have evolved a number of rules for construing contracts. These rules, however, are designed to assist the courts to interpret ambiguities or inconsistencies in a contract. Where the words of the contract are plain, the courts will not be persuaded to do any intellectual gymnastics for the purpose of giving the words some meaning other than their natural and ordinary meaning. This principle applies even where the meaning contended for is more fair and reasonable than the natural and ordinary meaning of the words. The principle is only departed from where to give words their natural and ordinary meaning would create, not merely an unreasonable result, but a result which would be inconsistent with, or absurd in the light of, the rest of the contract.[1]

Technical words in a contract are given by the courts their technical meaning unless there is a strong indication in the contract that the contrary was intended by the parties.[2] The courts sometimes take cognizance of local customs or usage, or the custom of a particular trade, in order to determine the meaning of words which have special meanings in that usage. The fact that such a custom exists, however, does not by itself prove that the parties intended to use particular words in the sense of that custom. It is a question of fact in each case whether or not the meaning of particular words in a contract is governed by trade or local usage.[3]

Some of the more important rules used to construe contracts which are ambiguous or inconsistent are: The intention of the parties has to be collected from the whole of the contract, and

[1] *Abbott* v. *Middleton* (1858) 7 H.L.C. 68 at p. 69.

[2] *Michael Borys* v. *Canadian Pacific Railway* [1953] A.C. 217.

[3] *Clayton* v. *Gregson* (1836) 5 A. & E. 302.

particular clauses which are ambiguous must be construed in the context of the whole document.[1] Draft contracts and negotiations leading up to a contract cannot be used to interpret the contract itself,[2] but, where a standard form of contract is used, the court may look at words in the form which have been deleted by the parties in order to resolve ambiguities in the remainder.[3] Where a form of contract is used with printed words together with other words written by hand or typewritten, the handwritten or typewritten words prevail over the printed words if there is any inconsistency between the two.[4] The courts will add to, delete from, or transfer words or cure grammatical errors in a contract in order to construe the contract in a way which carries out the lawful intentions of the parties.[5] Where in a contract several words of precise meaning are followed by words of a more general character (e.g. clause 28 of the I.C.E. conditions of contract: "... any patent rights design trade-marks or name or *other protected rights* ... all tonnage and other royalties, rent *and other payments* ... stone, sand, gravel, clay, *or other materials* ...") and the words of precise meaning are of a common category, the general words will not be construed as extending in effect beyond subjects in the same category (i.e. in the last mentioned example *other materials* will be construed as limited to materials in the same category as "stone, sand, gravel, and clay", that is to say, other materials occurring naturally in the ground).[6]

If an ambiguity cannot otherwise be resolved, the court will construe the contract strictly against the party responsible for drawing it up and liberally in favour of the party who has had no hand in its draftsmanship. There is no room for application of

---

[1] *North Eastern Railways* v. *Hastings* [1900] A.C. 260, at p. 267.

[2] *Davis Contractors Ltd.* v. *Fareham District Council* [1956] A.C. 696, 721.

[3] *Louis Dreyfus et Cie* v. *Parnaso Cie Naviera S.A.* [1959] 1 Q.B. 498; [1960] 2 Q.B. 49 C.A.

[4] *Re L. Sutro & Co. and Heilbut, Symons & Co.* [1917] 2 K.B. 348 at pp. 358, 361.

[5] *Gwyn* v. *Neath Canal Co.* (1865) L.R. 3 Ex. 209, at p. 215.

[6] *Att. Gen.* v. *Brown* [1920] 1 K.B. 773.

this rule, of course, where one or other of the standard forms of building or civil engineering contract has been used. But the rule has been applied to a case where a building contractor himself chose to draw up the conditions of contract.[1] The rule has likewise been applied against a local authority employer which chose to use a printed from of contract of its own devising.[2]

The two last-mentioned cases should cause parties to reflect before jettisoning the standard forms.

Express and Implied Terms

The terms of a contract are either express or implied. *Express terms*, as the name indicates, are those terms of the contract which the parties express in words either orally or in the contractual documents. An *implied term* is a term, which although not mentioned by the parties, is present in both their minds at the time they make the contract and which the court implies from the circumstances, or the parties' course of dealing, in order to fill a gap in the contract. This does not mean that the courts will be ready to imply terms to fill every gap which the parties may have left in their contract. The courts are in fact reluctant to imply terms, particularly in contracts as comprehensive as the standard forms used in civil engineering. The general rule is that the parties are presumed to have expressed in their contract all the terms which they intend should govern their business relations. The courts will, however, imply a term if it is necessary to give the contract *business efficacy*, and when it is clear that the parties both intended such a term to regulate their dealings.[3] The test of whether a term can properly be implied is often called by lawyers *the officious bystander test* (derived from a dictum of Lord Justice

---

[1] *Billyack* v. *Leyland Construction Co. Ltd.* [1968] 1 W.L.R. 471.

[2] *Peak Construction (Liverpool) Ltd.* v. *McKinney Foundations Ltd.* (1970) 1 B.L.R. 111.

[3] *The Moorcock* (1889) 14 P.D. 64.

Scrutton).[1] If, when the parties were making their contract, an imaginary bystander had said to them "what about so-and-so?" or "what about providing for such-and-such a situation?", and the parties had silenced him by saying, "that goes without saying", the term which "went without saying" will be implied into the contract. The courts generally imply into building and civil engineering contracts the terms that the employer will give the contractor possession of the site within a reasonable time,[2] that the employer will appoint an architect or engineer (if the contract contemplates the supervision of the work by an architect or engineer),[3] that the employer will not prevent the contractor from completing the works,[4] and that the contractor will do the work in a good and workmanlike manner.[5] In the standard forms of civil engineering contract all these matters are the subject of express terms. The courts will never imply a term into a contract which conflicts with an express term. Nor, where the express terms of the contract are clear and unambiguous, will the courts imply a term to mitigate the harshness of some consequence of the application of the express terms which the parties may have overlooked.[6] The courts will usually (but not invariably) imply terms into building and civil engineering contracts that the materials used by the contractor will be of reasonable quality and fit for the purpose for which they are required.[7]

---

[1] *Reigate* v. *Union Manufacturing Co. (Ramsbottom) Ltd.* [1918] 1 K.B. 592, at p. 605; *Wettern Electric Ltd.* v. *Welsh Development Agency* [1983] 2 W.L.R. 897.

[2] *Freeman* v. *Hensler* [1900] H.B.C. (4th Ed.). Vol. 2, p. 292.

[3] *Hunt* v. *Bishop* (1853) 8 Ex. 675.

[4] *William Cory Ltd.* v. *City of London Corporation* [1951] 2 K.B. 476.

[5] *Pearce* v. *Tucker* (1862) 3 F. & F. 136.

[6] *Trollope & Colls Ltd.* v. *North West Metropolitan Regional Hospital Board* [1973] 1 W.L.R. 601.

[7] *Gloucestershire County Council* v. *Richardson* [1969] 1 A.C. 480 H.L.; *Young & Marten Ltd.* v. *McManus Childs Ltd.* [1969] 1 A.C. 454 H.L.; *Norta* v. *John Sisk* (1977) 14. B.L.R. 49.

Rectification

If parties enter into a contract but there is an error, either by way of omission or misstatement, in their written contract so that the contractual document or documents do not accurately set out their common intention, the courts will correct the written contract so as to make it conform to what they intended to say. This remedy is called *rectification*. If both parties agree that their written contract is inaccurate, and agree upon the form of correction to be made, there is, of course, no need to have recourse to the courts. In these circumstances the parties may rectify the contract themselves. —▸ ADR .

Where, however, one party wishes to correct the contract and the other refuses, the party who insists upon the correction has to take proceedings for rectification. The Plaintiff in such proceedings must adduce evidence that leaves no fair or reasonable doubt that the written contract does not embody the common intention of the parties.[1] It is insufficient for him to show that the contract does not accurately represent his own intentions; he must show that the mistake was common to both sides. He must also specify the precise amendment which he wishes the court to make to the contract.

There is one exception to the rule the mistake must be common to both sides. If a written contract fails to represent the common intention of the parties because of the mistake of one party, and the other party knows of the mistake but keeps silent about it, the other party cannot resist a claim for rectification.[2] This is because the party who kept silent about his knowledge of the mistake is, by his conduct, prevented in the legal proceedings (or *estopped* in legal language) from denying the mistake.[3]

Claims for rectification are from time to time made where the contract is to do works for the contract sum, and arithmetical errors in the bills of quantities produce a contract sum which is

---

[1] *Crane* v. *Hegeman-Harris Inc.* [1939] 1 All E.R. 662; [1939] 4 All E.R. 68 (C.A.).

[2] *George Cohen & Sons* v. *Docks Executive* (1950) 84 Ll. L.R. 97.

[3] *Thomas Bates Ltd.* v. *Wyndham's Ltd.* [1981] 1 W.L.R. 505.

less than the true total of the bills, and where the contractor signs the contract in ignorance of the errors. It is unlikely that the contractor would succeed in a claim for rectification based on these facts alone, for he would not be able to establish that the contract misrepresented the common intention of the parties. If, however, the employer knew of the mistake and kept it from the contractor, and at that same time was aware that the contractor believed the contract sum to be the true total of the bills, the case would be otherwise.

Mistakes which give rise to a claim for rectification must be distinguished from mistakes so fundamental as to render the contract altogether void. The subjects of contracts void for mistake or illegality, or voidable on account of misrepresentation, are beyond the scope of this book. A summary of the law on these subjects as it affects civil engineering contracts may be found in *Hudson's Building and Engineering Contracts* (10th ed.), pp. 24–29 and 316–7.[1]

Waiver

Where one party to a contract leads the other party reasonably to believe that in some respect legal rights under the contract will not be insisted upon, his conduct constitutes a *waiver* of the rights in questions.[2] A waiver may be in writing, or oral, or inferred from conduct, notwithstanding that the contract is in writing.[3] Difficulties sometimes arise when a civil engineering contract provides that extras shall not be paid for unless ordered in writing by the consultant, and the employer himself orders extras and takes the benefit of them. In these circumstances the courts are likely to hold that the employer has waived the contractual term about the ordering of extras, and has made an implied promise to pay the contractor for the extra work.[4]

[1] Published 1970, Sweet & Maxwell.

[2] *Rickards* v. *Openheim* [1950] 1 K.B. 616 a p. 626.

[3] *Besseler Waechter Glover & Co.* v. *South Derwent Coal Co.* [1938] 1 K.B. 408 at pp. 416–17.

[4] *Taverner* v. *Glamorgan County Council* (1941) 57 T.L.R. 243; *Molloy* v. *Liebe* (1910) 102 L.T. 616.

Work Done before Contract

A cause of dispute which sometimes occurs in relation to building and civil engineering work is where, because of the urgency of the need to begin the work, or for other reasons, work is done by the contractor while the contract is still under negotiation and before any binding agreement is made which regulates the rights and duties of the parties. The approach of the courts to the problems to which this situation gives rise may be illustrated by reference to two such cases. In the first, a builder submitted a tender for the reconstruction of war-damaged premises. No binding contract was made but the builder was led to believe by the employer that he would receive the contract. At the request of the employer's surveyor, the builder prepared various estimates, bills of quantities, and schedules of timber and steel requirements which were of use to the employer in negotiating with the War Damage Commission. Although no binding contract was ever concluded the court held that there was an implied promise by the employer to pay the builder reasonable remuneration for this work.[1]

In the second case sub-contractors submitted to the main contractors a tender for the carrying out of civil engineering works in the building of a nuclear power station. The tender was for a lump sum price, but incorporated conditions authorizing the main contractors to make variations in the works, and providing that the price should be adjusted for such variations and for fluctuations in the cost of labour and materials. Substantial changes in the works were made after the submission of the tender. The sub-contractors began work on the project at the request of the main contractors, but, although both parties intended that a binding contract should be made between them, they did not reach agreement on the essential terms of the contract until ten months after the work had been started. The sub-contractors claimed that they were entitled to be paid reasonable remuneration for the work they had done regardless of the terms subsequently agreed. The court held,

[1] *William Lacey (Hounslow) Ltd.* v. *Davis* [1957] 1 W.L.R. 932. See also *Peter Lind & Co. Ltd.* v. *Mersey Docks & Harbour Board* [1972] 2 Lloyd's Rep. 234.

however, that the parties had acted in the course of the negotiations on the understanding that, if and when a contract was made, it would govern what was being done meanwhile, and that the subsequent contract regulated retrospectively the rights and duties of the parties in respect of the work done prior to it.[1]

The most difficult case of this kind would appear to be one which falls, as it were, between the two described above, that is to say where the parties move some way towards agreeing upon terms but do not reach agreement on all essential terms, and where work is begun meanwhile. The question then arises, whether those terms upon which agreement is reached govern the rights and duties of the parties in respect of the prior work. This question is discussed earlier under the heading "Battle of Forms". It may follow from the comments of Lord Denning, M.R. in *Butler Machine Tool* v. *Ex-Cell-O Corporation*[2] that those terms which have been agreed will bind the parties, whilst those terms not agreed will be replaced by a reasonable implication.[3]

Arbitration

Justice, by its nature, has to be thorough. Because it is thorough it often tends to be slow. A High Court action relating to a civil engineering project may engage the full attention of a substantial number of skilled men, counsel, solicitors, expert witnesses and others, for a substantial length of time at the trial and in all the necessary preparations for trial. For this reason litigation is expensive, and cautious men do their best to avoid it.

The process of submitting a dispute to arbitration may or may not be cheaper than litigation. Where the issue is mainly concerned with points of law which the parties are determined to have resolved eventually by a court of law, arbitration offers

---

[1] *Trollope & Colls Ltd.* v. *Atomic Power Constructions Ltd.* [1963] 1 W.L.R. 333.

[2] [1979] 1 W.L.R. 401.

[3] See p. 26.

little or no advantage. Generally, however, the process of arbitration offers considerable advantages in disputes arising out of civil engineering contracts. Where the arbitrator appointed has personal knowledge and experience of civil engineering, the need to call expert witnesses and the need to explain technical matters is lessened or avoided. In this way the length of the hearing may be much shortened and costs accordingly reduced.

On the other hand it should always be remembered that the time of an arbitrator, unlike that of a judge, must be paid for by the parties, and that accommodation must be provided for the hearing.

The standard forms and conditions of contract referred to in this book invariably contain a clause requiring the parties to submit disputes to arbitration. The jurisdiction of an arbitrator depends upon the precise wording of the clause used. In general, however, it can be said that under the clauses in common use in civil engineering contracts the arbitrator has jurisdiction to determine whether one or other of the parties has broken or repudiated the contract;[1] to determine whether the contract has been frustrated, and, if so, the rights of the parties arising as a result,[2] to determine disputes about extras,[3] to open up, review or revise a certificate; and to decide questions of law.

It was previously thought that the court had the same powers as an arbitrator to review and revise certificates. However, the position was recently stated and clarified in the dictum of the Court of Appeal in a case concerning the 1963 J.C.T. form. Where the parties have agreed that disputes as to anything left to the discretion of the architect should be referred to arbitration by means of machinery such as that in Clause 35 of the J.C.T. form it is not for the court to intervene and replace its own process for the contractual machinery agreed by the parties. Thus the court has no power to open up, review or revise any certificate, opinion, or decision of the architect unless the contractual machinery has broken down.[4] The Court

---

[1] *Heyman* v. *Darwins Ltd.* [1942] A.C. 356.

[2] *Government of Gibraltar* v. *Kenny* [1956] 2 Q.B. 410.

[3] *Heyman* v. *Darwins Ltd.* [1942] A.C. 356.

[4] *Northern Regional Health Authority* v. *Derek Crouch Construction Ltd.* [1984] 2 W.L.R. 676.

is, however, empowered to declare that any certificate or opinion is invalid if the architect had no power to give such certificate or opinion or had otherwise erred in law in giving it.[1]

The arbitrator does not have jurisdiction to decide whether or not the contract which contains the arbitration clause is void[2] or whether he has jurisdiction upon any question.[3]

Arbitration clauses commonly provide that the decision of the arbitrator shall be final and binding on the parties. A provision, however, that the parties may not have recourse at all to a court of law, even when the arbitrator is mistaken in law, is void.[4] The broad effect of this principle and the relevant provisions of the Arbitration Acts, 1950 and 1979, is to reserve to the parties a right of appeal from an arbitrator to the courts on a point of law, (although not on a point of fact), if all parties consent or leave is given by the court. There is, however, provision in s.3 Arbitration Act, 1979 for the parties to an arbitration to enter into an exclusion agreement which excludes their rights to appeal to the court. If one party to a contract which contains an arbitration clause breaks the arbitration agreement by bringing an action upon the contract in the courts, the other party may apply to the courts to stay the action.[5]

Private International Law

The law referred to in this chapter and throughout this book is the law of England. The relevant law in those Commonwealth countries and those states of the United States of America which have adopted the common law system is in many respects similar to that described here. The law of contract in European and many other countries, however, is markedly different. Questions frequently arise, not least in relation to civil

[1] Ibid at page 691.

[2] *Heyman* v. *Darwins* [1942] A.C. 356.

[3] *Smith* v. *Martin* [1925] 1 K.B. 745.

[4] *Lee* v. *The Showmen's Guild* [1952] 2 Q.B. 329.

[5] Arbitration Act, 1950 (14 Geo. VI, c. 27), s. 4.

engineering contracts, as to which system of law is applicable to a particular contract and as to which country's courts the contract may be enforced in. To answer these questions from the point of view of English law it is necessary to make a brief reference to the branch of English law known as *Private International Law* or the *Conflict of Laws*.

In general, anyone may sue or be sued in the courts of England, whatever his nationality or domicile, and regardless of where the cause of action arose or where the subject matter of action is situated. The only class of persons who cannot sue in the English courts are enemy aliens. There are however a large number of exceptions to the rule that anyone may be sued. A person (other than a foreign sovereign) may be sued in the English courts if he is present in England or Wales,[1] or if he voluntarily submits to the jurisdiction of the English courts.[2] A corporation is *present in England or Wales* if it does business in England or Wales.[3] If the proposed defendant is neither present within nor voluntarily submits to the jurisdiction he may only be made a party to an action to enforce, rescind, dissolve, annul or otherwise effect a contract, or to recover damages for, or other relief, in respect of a breach of contract in the following cases:

1. Where the contract is made in England, and the defendant is neither domiciled nor ordinarily resident in Scotland.
2. Where the contract is made by or through an agent trading or residing in England on behalf of a principal trading or residing out of England, provided that the defendant is neither domiciled nor ordinarily resident in Scotland.
3. Where the contract is by its terms or by implication to be governed by English law, provided that the defendant is neither domiciled nor ordinarily resident in Scotland.
4. Where the action is in respect of a breach, which has in fact been committed in England, of a contract wherever made, even though the English breach has been preceded by a breach abroad which rendered impossible of performance

[1] *John Russell & Co. Ltd.* v. *Cayzer, Irvine & Co. Ltd.* [1916] 2 A.C. 298.
[2] *Feyerick* v. *Hubbard* (1902) 71 L.J.K.B. 509.
[3] *Okura & Co. Ltd.* v. *Forsbacka Jernverks Aktirbolag* [1914] 1 K.B. 715.

that part of the contract which ought to have been performed in England.[1]

The place where a contract is made is the place where the contract is made binding by the communication of an acceptance. Thus, according to the rules elaborated earlier in this chapter, where acceptance is made by letter posted in England addressed to the other party in a country abroad, the place of the making of the contract is, in the eyes of English law, England.

It does not necessarily follow from the fact that the English courts have jurisdiction to entertain an action for, say, damages for breach of a particular civil engineering contract at the suit of one of the parties that the system of law according to which the English court will determine the issue will be English law. The English courts from time to time determine issues according to the laws of foreign countries, for which purpose they hear expert evidence of the relevant foreign law from lawyers qualified in the appropriate country. Where contracts are made abroad, or are written in foreign languages, or contain references to foreign laws, difficult questions may arise as to the choice of law to be applied.

Such matters are beyond the scope of this book and reference should be made to one of the standard texts on *Conflicts of Law* and *Private International Law*. It is important to note here, however, that these problems may be largely circumvented if the parties to a civil engineering contract which has connections with more than one country insert in their contract a clause stating expressly which legal system should govern their rights and duties.[2]

European Communities Law

The United Kingdom has been a Member State of the European Communities since 1 January 1973. Membership

[1] R.S.C., Order 11, rule 1.

[2] *Vita Food Products Inc.* v. *Unus Shipping Co.* [1939] A.C. 277, at p. 290.

obliges it to accept the laws made by the Council and Commission of the European Communities, and to promote the objectives for which the European Communities were established. There are important provisions of the E.E.C. Treaty dealing with "the rights of establishment" and "the right to provide services", i.e. the rights of nationals of a Member State to establish themselves and provide services in the territory of another Member State.[1] From these provisions stem a set of E.E.C. rules governing public works contracts. The object of the rules is to abolish restrictions on the freedom of persons throughout the Community, irrespective of nationality, to tender for and be awarded public service contracts. In addition the rules are aimed at securing effective competition in the field of public service contracts and introducing common criteria for the award of contracts.

The European Communities Civil Jurisdiction and Judgement Act, 1982 which is expected to come into force during 1985 after it has been finally ratified by all the member countries, allows individuals and corporations to be sued in the country in which they reside. Enforcement thereby being made easier.

---

[1] E.E.C. Treaty, Articles 52–66.

CHAPTER 3

TYPES OF CONTRACT AND THEIR STANDARD FORMS

Types of Contract

The price to be paid for civil engineering and building works can be determined either by measurement and valuation, or on the basis of the actual cost incurred by the contractor.

The various types of contracts used for measurement are known collectively as lump sum or fixed price contracts, although this term is also used to describe contracts that do not contain a clause protecting the contractor from most of the risks arising from fluctuation in the market prices of materials and increases in the nationally agreed wages rates. Both applications are misleading, for it is most unusual for the tender price to coincide with the final amount to be paid, except in the case of small works, and the term is not intended to imply a fixed total contract price. Contracts which are paid for on the basis of the money spent in carrying out the works are known as cost reimbursement contracts. In addition, there are several hybrid forms of contract which either contain elements of both the fixed price and cost reimbursement contract, or make at least a part of the design a factor in the tender price. In principle, a choice must be made of one of these types of contract before preparation of the tender documents is put in hand. Frequently past experience makes the choice obvious, but sometimes it will be necessary to compare the relative merits of the different types before selection. Besides agreeing upon a type of contract, it is necessary to decide upon the form of contract to be used. There are alternative standard forms available and the choice will depend in part on whether civil engineering or building work predominates, and also on the status of the promoter, because sometimes local authorities and often government departments have their own standard forms.

Standard Forms of Contract

The standard forms of contracts in general use are:

1. *Conditions of Contract and Forms of Tender, Agreement and Bond for use in connection with Works of Civil Engineering Construction, 5th Ed. (June 1973)* – commonly known as "the I.C.E. Conditions of Contract" – It is suited for use with bills of quantities and schedule contracts. The Institution of Civil Engineers, the Association of Consulting Engineers and the Federation of Civil Engineering Contractors are the sponsors.

2. *"Standard Form of Building Contract". Local Authorities with Quantities.* 1980 Edition – commonly known as the J.C.T. 1980 contract – is issued by the Constituent bodies of the Joint Contracts Tribunal and published by the R.I.B.A. Publications Ltd. It is drafted for use with bills of quantities contracts.

3. *"Standard Form of Building Contract". Private Edition with Quantities* 1980 Edition – is issued by the J.C.T. and its conditions differ only slightly from the local authorities "Standard Form".

4. *"Standard Forms of Building Contract" Local Authorities Edition with Approximate Quantities* 1980 Edition – the modification of the J.C.T. Standard Form with Quantities for use with approximate quantities.

5. *Standard Form of Building Contract – Private Edition with Approximate Quantities* – differs only slightly from the local authorities "Standard Form".

6. *"Standard Form" of Building Contract – Local Authorities without Quantities* 1980 Edition – is issued by the

J.C.T. It is drafted for use with lump sum contracts without quantities.

7. *"Standard Form" of Building Contract Private Edition without Quantities* 1980 Edition – an adaptation of the previous form.

8. *Fixed Fee Form of Prime Cost Building Contract* Local Authorities Edition (1967 Current revision) issued by the J.C.T.

9. *Fixed Fee Form of Prime Cost Building Contract* Private Edition 1967 (Current revision) issued by the J.C.T.

10. *Agreement for Minor Building Works (not for use in Scotland)* 1980 (reprint with corrections 1981) issued by J.C.T. is suitable for small value contracts, and does not have clauses relating to nominated sub-contractors.

11. *Contractor's Designed Portion Supplement (1981) for use with the Standard Form of Building Contract with Quantities, Local Authorities and Private 1980 Editions* issued by the J.C.T. and contains the amendments to be made to both "the with Quantities Forms".

12. *Model Form of General Conditions of Contract for use in connection with Home Contracts – with erection.* The Institution of Electrical Engineers, the Institution of Mechanical Engineers and the Association of Consulting Engineers are the sponsoring bodies.

13. *General Conditions of Government Contracts for Building and Civil Engineering Works – Edition 2*, published by H.M.S.O.

14. *General Conditions of Government Contracts for Building, Civil Engineering, Mechanical and Electrical Small Works* published by H.M.S.O.

15. *A.C.A. Form of Building Agreement, 1982 sponsored by the Association of Consultant Architects*, published by the Architectural Press Ltd. (a new and improved version was published in 1984)

16. *Intermediate Form of Contract, 1984 issued by the J.C.T.*, not considered suitable for contracts subject to Scottish Law and not to be recommended elsewhere for works that include nominated sub-contracts.

These are the standard forms most often used for constructional work, and each one has been framed for use with a particular class of work. The I.C.E. form and J.C.T. quantities forms are more widely accepted than the others. It is the duty of the consulting engineer to advise the client upon the selection of the standard form best suited to his requirements.

On their introduction, the J.C.T. 1980 contracts did not receive a general welcome from either consultants or clients. Reservations were expressed about the removal of the option to delete the clauses which allow an extension of time because of shortage of labour and material,[1] and the procedures for the selection and appointment of nominated sub-contractors. These difficulties, while not to be under-estimated, have proved in practice not more awkward than those which sometimes plagued earlier versions of the J.C.T. contract. Yet, as a result of these earlier misgivings, the Association of Consultant Architects have issued a form of contract which offers an alternative to those who are not prepared to use J.C.T. 80 until others have acquired more experience of its use in practice[2] and do not want to use the older J.C.T. contracts by use of cross-reference to clause-headings. Difficulties inherent in construction work cannot be exorcised by contract clauses. The advantages of the J.C.T. 80 contracts are an improvement in procedures which provide firmer constraints on both parties to the contract, and the consultants, making it more likely that the difficulties will not get out of control, and less likely that the parties will find it impossible to conclude their dispute without resort to the law court. The revised edition of the A.C.A. contract also provides constraints on those concerned with the contract and has fewer clauses than the J.C.T. form. The A.C.A. Form of Building Agreement, 1982, sponsored by the Association of Consultant Architects and published by the Architectural Press is the most recent of forms to become available. It offers the following alternative procedures:

[1] J.C.T. 80 – Clause 25.4.10.1 and 2

[2] Time-scales for the legal history of contracts can sometimes extend beyond ten years.

(1) It can be used with or without quantities.
(2) All drawings are to be provided by the architect or he provides a "finite set" of drawings, and all further drawings required are prepared by the contractor.
(3) Grounds for extension of time are limited to acts or omissions of the employer or his representative or extensions of time are allowed for a restricted number of grounds which exclude exceptionally adverse weather conditions, industrial action, and scarcity of material and labour.

This form has been subject to some criticism, and has not received the approval of the bodies who sponsor the J.C.T. 80 contracts, but it has been welcomed by some organizations in the private sector.

Occasionally, the engineer may find that a client will suggest numerous special conditions amending the general conditions such as to render them more favourable to the client, or the use of a form of contract and conditions drafted by his legal advisers, or in the case of foreign clients he may be asked to use an unfamiliar form. Unless there are very good reasons to the contrary, he should do all within his power to persuade his client to use one of the standard forms previously mentioned or a recognized overseas form. Normally it can be expected that contractors will increase their prices to allow for the additional risks that they consider arise when an unusual form of contract is adopted, and it should be explained to the client that his best interests are served by the use of a generally accepted standard form. Sometimes the advice of the professional adviser on these matters is ignored, and there are the rare instances when the use of unfamiliar contract conditions are justified. The engineer will then have the task of scrutinizing the conditions to ensure that all the conditions essential to the contract are included, and that unfair clauses are modified. In addition there are other standard forms of contract for use in specialized works such as the I.C.E. Conditions of Contract for ground investigation; the Form of Sub-Contract (Blue Form) published by the Federation of Civil Engineering Contractors, and the Form of Sub-

Contract published by the Confederation of Building Trade Employers.

Conditions of Contract

The primary clauses in any constructional contract are as follows:

1. Duties and power of site representative.
2. Limitations on assignment and sub-letting.
3. Definition of contract documents.
4. Superintendence to be provided by contractor.
5. Responsibility for setting out work.
6. Watching and lighting.
7. Contractor's liability to indemnify employer for damages to persons and property.
8. Insurances.
9. Notices and fees.
10. Damage to highways and bridges.
11. Testing and substantiation of quality of material and workmanship.
12. Removal of defective work.
13. Completion certificate, time for completion, and defects liability period.
14. Engineer's instructions.
15. Bills of quantities, variations, dayworks, and valuation of completed work.
16. Ownership of unfixed material and plant.
17. Provisional and prime cost sums and nominated sub-contractors.
18. Certificates, payments, and retention.
19. Determination of contract.
20. Frustration.
21. Arbitration procedure.

Further clauses may be necessary, and the engineer should compare the clauses in the special contract conditions with those in the comparable standard form; and also check that the clauses are neither ambiguous, nor incomplete, nor contrary to good practice, and are suited to the type of contract selected.

Consideration should always be given to the advisability of incorporating a fluctuations or price variations clause in the conditions of all measurement and lump sum contracts. Fluctuation clauses permit any increases or decreases in the market price of materials or the official rates of labour to be added or deducted from the contract sum. Decision on their inclusion in the contract will be determined by the duration of the contract and the extent to which the contractor can confidently predict his material, plant, and labour requirements at the time of the tender. It is usual to incorporate a fluctuation clause in all contracts whose duration exceeds two years. Contracts which can be completed in a shorter time should include such a clause when it is not possible to provide accurate drawings and quantities at the tender stage, or when prices and wages lack even short term stability. In special cases the fluctuation clause can be limited to price variations in either wages or materials. Prices are likely to be inflated by tenderers when they are called upon to give firm prices for a contract extending over a long period.[1]

However it should be borne in mind that the use of fluctuation clauses increases the cost of administering the submission and certification of monthly statements.

Lump Sum Contracts without Quantities

The simplest type of constructional contract is the lump sum contract without quantities. Drawings, specification and the contract conditions will comprise the contract documents. The tender price will be determined by the contractor from the drawings and specification by any method he chooses. Sometimes he will prepare a detailed bill of quantities which he will then price to obtain the lump sum, or he may use one of the many systems of approximate estimating to calculate his price.

[1] See pp. 127, 218.

Quantities are sometimes included in, or annexed to, the specification and to the extent that they are incorporated in the specification form part of the contract. The tenderer is responsible for obtaining his own quantities from the drawing and takes responsibility for their accuracy. Difficulties do occur when it is not possible for the contractor to estimate accurately the value of some small part of the work; this is especially so with repair and maintenance contracts. Tenderers for a road-resurfacing contract should be able readily to calculate accurate quantities for the new surfacing required, but they cannot be expected to know the amount of making good required to the sub-surface, nor should they always be asked to take the risk of speculating on the cost of making good. An alternative is to agree to a daywork valuation of these items, based on the hours worked and quantities of materials used,[1] but this is often undesirable.

The problem may be overcome by the inclusion of provisional quantities in the specification of these doubtful items, providing the wording of the conditions of the contract is amended to allow for the adjustment of the quantities after the work has been carried out.

Generally alterations to the standard conditions should be avoided, as alterations are considered by the professions and the contractor's associations to cause difficulties in interpretation, leading to problems at law. Yet circumstances may compel the engineer to ignore this golden rule when faced with technical problems of this kind.

A precise and adequate specification with accurate drawings is essential for obtaining satisfactory tenders for these lump sum contracts without quantities. When the drawings give a mere outline of the scheme, and the specification leaves minor details to the discretion of the contractor, it is important that a standard specification, code of practice, or by-laws giving either standard of performance or regulations for the design is cited or incorporated in the specification. Usually specifications for constructional works describe the materials and workmanship

[1] See p. 91.

in detail and only occasionally frame the requirements on the basis of a standard of performance. Specifications which leave open the design, choice of material, and method of workmanship to the contractor, and give the requirements mainly in terms of a standard of performance, are more commonly used for electrical and mechanical installations. When individual contractors offer differing proprietary systems for piling works, suspended floors and other structural elements, it may be decided to call for tenders based on performance specifications. Performance specifications are only desirable when there is little or no limitation on the kinds of solution required. For instance, it would be pointless to invite tenders for a bridge to be prepared upon a performance specification when limitations on the span between supports, maintenance requirements, appearance, and method of construction predetermine the most practicable kind of design.[1] The engineer has less control over the execution of the work when it is carried out in accordance with a performance specification, and it is of special importance that the contractor chosen to do the work in these cases should be one of known reliability and integrity. Often the function of the installation or structure is not directly related to its useful life; and the performance specification should be qualified to include the specification of materials which reduce the maintenance costs.

For small works, the lump sum contract without quantities has the advantage of saving both the time and cost spent in preparing quantities; but variations are not as readily adjusted. A schedule of rates of the main items of work annexed to the contract will counteract this difficulty to a great extent, and the engineer should always ensure that a sufficiently detailed schedule of prices is provided by the successful tenderer and incorporated in the contract.

It must be emphasized that adjustments are made to the lump sum only for variations ordered by the engineer, and that no amendments can be made to it because of the overestimating or underestimating of quantities in the build-up of the original

---

[1] With the present competition between steel and concrete and the emphasis on low initial cost, alternative tenders for road bridges are now more frequently encouraged.

tender figure.

The two J.C.T. contracts without quantities are the only standard forms drafted especially for use with small lump sum contracts, although both the I.C.E. and GC/Works/1 conditions can be adapted for use with this type of contract. The choice will depend on whether the work is either predominantly of a civil engineering, or building, type.

The lump sum contract without quantities involves a duplication of effort expended in measuring when two or more firms are in competition; on small contracts this is not serious, but on large contracts it will increase tendering costs considerably. Neither civil engineering nor building contractors care to tender in competition without bills of quantities for contracts of large value. At one time the Confederation of Building Trade Employers recommended their members to refuse to tender in competition for works in excess of a certain value. This recommendation was withdrawn as a result of proceedings in the Restrictive Practices Court, although the individual contractor has still the right to decline an invitation where quantities are not provided. It will usually be in the client's interest for quantities to be provided for all work tendered for in competition, except those of small value. Even when the price is negotiated most contractors will expect a bill of quantities to be provided for large scale works.

Bills of Quantities Contract

Bills of quantities contracts are the second type of fixed price contract. Detailed bills of quantities are prepared in accordance with the *Civil Engineering Standard Method of Measurement, 1976* (referred to hereafter as the *C.E.S.M.M.*)[1] or, where building works predominate, in accordance with the *Standard Method of Measurement of Building Works*, 6th ed., 1978. These bills record and describe in some form or other every item of labour and material which goes into the work, and also list all the obligations of the contractor in respect of temporary

[1] A new edition of the *C.E.S.M.M.* has been prepared and will be published during 1985.

works, plant, supervision, insurances and his liabilities for defects after the completion of the works. Each tendering contractor receives a copy of these bills, and by pricing each item arrives at an aggregate value which constitutes the tender sum. This procedure not only saves the heavy cost of preparing many bills of quantities, but all contractors price identical bills, and the discrepancies which are likely to arise from differing interpretations of the drawings are avoided. The allocation of the estimated book cost and profit against individual items in the bills will depend on the methods and policies adopted by the individual contractor, and various permutations and combinations of the cost elements will be encountered. It is not unusual for contractors to leave unpriced at least a proportion of the items in the preliminary bill. The cost of these is added to the value of the items of labour and material in the main sections of the bill, and sometimes the whole cost of the preliminary items is apportioned among the measured items in the main bills.

The bills of quantities contracts are only adjusted in respect of variations. The I.C.E. form of contract cannot strictly be termed a bill of quantities contract because the quantities are not to be taken as the actual and correct quantities of the works, and is therefore known as an admeasurement contract. In normal day-to-day practice it can be accepted that the I.C.E. form of contract is a fixed price one which may be completely remeasured though no variations are ordered. The J.C.T. quantities contracts on the other hand are only subject to remeasurement in so far as they are varied, or the quantities are in error; but as no variation can vitiate the contract, they will, if necessary, be completely remeasured. The J.C.T. quantities contract can therefore be defined as a fixed price contract which can be completely remeasured and valued when the variations are extensive. Although at first sight these distinctions between the I.C.E. and J.C.T. contracts may appear to be fine ones, they have tangible effects on the preparation of the contract documents, and the settlement of the final account, as will be seen later.

Besides their primary purpose of providing an equitable basis for the preparation of tenders, the bills of quantities also provide a schedule of rates for the valuation of variations and the remeasured work. They have other useful subsidiary functions. The promoter is given an accurate forecast of his financial commitment providing there are no major variations. The engineer can estimate the likely cost of possible variations. For the contractor, the bills will often provide a guide when he is planning and programming the sequence of work. He may also use it for calculating targets, and for making bonus payments to the operatives in connection with incentive schemes. Bills of quantities contain a mass of information on cost, which, when analysed by the engineer or his quantity surveyor, can provide fundamental data which can be utilized for approximate estimates of the total cost of similar projects, and for comparative studies of the costs of alternative design solutions for structural and civil engineering schemes. The task of processing this information is formidable. It is only recently that systematic research has been undertaken to investigate the most efficient methods of obtaining and using to the fullest extent the unco-ordinated data available.

The quantities are prepared from drawings with the aid of a specification or specification notes. When the I.C.E. contract is used the specification is one of the contract documents, and it is important that ambiguities in or discrepancies between the drawings, quantities and specification are avoided. A civil engineering bill of quantities must provide quantities and information to enable the preparation of efficient and accurate tenders, and which will, after the commencement of the contract, enable the works in progress to be valued.

The *C.E.S.M.M.* states that work shall be itemized "in sufficient detail for it to be possible to distinguish between the different classes of work, and between work of the same nature carried out in different locations or in any other circumstances which may give rise to different considerations of cost", and that subject to these requirements the "layout and content of the Bills of Quantities should be as simple and brief as possible". Consequently the descriptions in the bills of quantities will not give the estimator sufficient information on which to base his price; and he must be able to obtain from the specification and drawings a definition of the exact nature of the work and the engineer's requirements. It is imperative that the specification clauses contain all the data required for ascertaining all matters affecting the cost of items listed in the bills, or that this data is provided in the form of preambles to the bill of quantities. The drafting of the descriptions in the bill of quantities to ensure the required combination of brevity and identification calls for skill and care.

When the J.C.T. quantities form of contract is used, the specification is not a contract document, and the bills of quantities must incorporate those portions of the specification which have a bearing on the cost of the work. In the case of structural engineering works, it will usually be necessary to incorporate the whole of the engineer's specification in the bills. This is achieved by giving the items in the bills more detailed descriptions, and by the inclusion of clauses defining the material and workmanship at the commencement of the relevant bill. There will be many more items in such bills of quantities, because the *Standard Method of Measurement of Building Works* calls for the measurement of many subsidiary items which are normally deemed to be included in a single item in an engineering bill. Each item in the bills for building works will be more fully described. Difficulties arise when a small amount of building work is contained in a predominantly civil engineering contract, or when the opposite occurs. It is suggested that the best procedure is to measure the untypical work in accordance with the method of measurement to which it belongs, provided that this section of the work is isolated in a separate bill, and the contractor is clearly warned of the departure from the predominant methods of measurement, and the contract is amended.

Obviously the drawings and specification from which the quantities are taken must contain sufficient information and detail to enable accurate quantities to be prepared. For although the quantities in civil engineering bills are only expected to be estimated, the civil engineering method of measurement makes it quite clear that a distinction must be made between quantities for that part of the work which is regarded as definite, and additional measurements and items included in the bill to cover the approximate cost of additional work which, although required, is not yet designed or detailed, and also the contingent quantities that must often be included to allow for the uncertainties associated with foundation and marine works. These provisional quantities must always be shown separately in the bills and not grouped with the remainder of the work. This rule is equally applicable to bills prepared for a J.C.T. quantities contract. There are no limitations on the proportion of provisional items allowed in the bills. But if the drawings are only unapproved preliminary drafts, and the major details of the scheme are still to be agreed, it will be impossible to prepare adequate quantities; and the adoption of a bill of quantities contract will be satisfactory neither for the promoter of the works nor for the contractor he employs.

Schedule Contracts

The third type of fixed price contract resolves the difficulties caused when the whole or a major part of the works is provisional. These are called schedule contracts. There is a wide variety of schedules ranging from the approximate bill of quantities, which when priced provides both a contract sum and schedule of prices on which the remeasurement can be based, to a schedule of items without quantities which become a price list for the valuation of the work eventually carried out. Sometimes the schedules are printed with the prices inserted, and the competing contractors arrive at their tender-figure by making percentage adjustment to these prices. Adjustment is made usually for each section of the work, and not for individual items, or for the whole of the bills. The same standard forms of contract as are used for bills of quantities are employed for these schedule contracts. Amendments are made to the clauses relevant to measurement to meet the particular requirements of the type of schedule contract adopted.

This procedure permits the preparation of quantities from

preliminary drawings without delay. While these quantities will not be accurate, they should normally enable a contractor to visualize the scope of the contract, and to give a realistic price for the work. A forecast of the client's financial liability of the order of accuracy associated with an accurate bill of quantities is not to be expected; but a tender based on approximate quantities will, if prepared from drawings showing the main outlines of the scheme, provide an estimate of the probable cost upon which the client can base policy decisions and give him guidance when budgeting. However, much will depend on the cost control exercised by his professional advisers from the preparation of the initial scheme to the completion of the works. The preparation of satisfactory approximate bills from the preliminary small scale drawings calls for a skill compounded of experience and forethought, because the bills should include, in addition to those items shown on the drawings, other items which can only be implied from the information recorded on the drawings. These items may concern costly work. The preliminary details of a wharf may show the steel sheet piling, tie rods, anchor walls and cope, and omit information about the gantries, cranes and rail track required, and the dredging and consolidation of the ground by a geotechnical process which forms an integral part of the scheme. In some classes of work there may be hazards encountered about which only the vaguest predictions can be made. The engineer must choose between ignoring them altogether or making some estimate of the work involved. Usually it is best to make some modest provision for these eventualities in preference either to ignoring them or assuming the worst case. The promoter must be warned of the possible extra costs he will incur if the difficulties met with prove more extensive than provided for in the bills.

A further advantage of the schedules is that they can be prepared without delay for projects of long duration. During the execution of the early phases of the scheme, accurate bills of quantities can be prepared for the remainder of the work. These can be priced on the basis of the original schedule by the contractor already working at the site, or competitive tenders can be obtained, and if necessary another firm can carry out the later phases. For example, the foundations of a power station could be measured and valued in accordance with a schedule of rates; while the remainder of the structure would be the subject of a bill of quantities contract; or approximate quantities could be utilized for the first and possibly experimental portion of a road or railway scheme, while accurate bills are prepared for the main scheme. Difficulties in demarcating the responsibilities for defects will be met when two contractors are concerned with the construction of one scheme; and a pause in the progress of the works will inevitably occur in the transition period when a new contractor takes over the site. These disadvantages must be assessed in relation to the particular problems of each project, and a decision made as to the merits of the alternative procedures.

The schedule contract also enables contractor and engineer to co-operate at the design stage in the pioneering of new techniques economically. The schedules of prices should be negotiated at an early stage to give the contractor and the consultant an opportunity to discuss the relationship of the use of plant and organization of the work to the design. Schedule contracts are frequently used for repair and maintenance works, and in many ways they are probably the type of contract most suitable for this class of work, providing the task of measuring does not present special difficulties.

Cost Reimbursement Contracts

Contracts which are paid for on the basis of the money spent in carrying out the work are called cost reimbursement contracts. They should only be used when it is not reasonable to ask the contractor to estimate the value of the work because the scope cannot be predetermined. These contracts take two typical forms. The first is known as the cost plus percentage contract. The cost will be the aggregate of the money expended in wages, materials, plant, consumable stores, services and haulage, together with the amounts of sub-contractors' accounts, to which is added a percentage for profit and overheads. There is a divergence of practice on the treatment of certain marginal items; in some cases they are included in the cost, and in others they are covered by percentage additions for profit and overheads. It is therefore of the utmost importance that the conditions of the contract should clearly state the intention of the parties on these points. Normally, head office costs are included in the percentage, but the expenses of visiting management staff and the salaries or wages of clerks resident at the site can either be included in the cost or covered by the percentage.

There is no standard scale of percentage additions applicable to cost contracts, and this addition must either be negotiated with the contractor, or several contractors can be invited to tender in competition, and the contract awarded to the tenderer offering to carry out the work for the lowest percentage. Percentages offered will be influenced both by the prospective value of the work, and the range of the items excluded from the cost. Usually the contractor will expect higher percentages for small contracts, as well as when the work involves him in drawing office and head office costs above average. Sometimes different percentages are applied to labour, material and plant costs, and almost invariably a smaller percentage is added to the accounts of sub-contractors.

The inherent defect of the cost plus percentage contract is that it gives a contractor no financial incentive to control his cost. In fact minimum efficiency maximizes his profit. For this reason it does not provide a reliable basis for obtaining competitive tenders as the contractor who offers to do the work for the lowest percentage may be much less efficient than his competitors who seek a higher fee. In such cases it is probable that despite the higher percentage fee, the final cost will be less. Despite these unattractive features, this type of contract may prove under some conditions to be the most suitable, and may be the only reasonable method of dealing with exploratory and emergency works.

The alternative type of cost reimbursement contract, known as the cost plus fixed fee contract, is designed to reward the most efficient contractor, for although the cost will be calculated in the same way as the percentage fee contract, the allowance for the contractor's profit and overheads is predetermined by computation of a fixed fee, with the result that fluctuations in the cost neither diminish nor increase the sum paid to cover profit and overheads, although the reduction in cost will increase the percentage of profit, and reduce overhead costs. An estimate is usually made of the probable net cost, an agreed percentage of which is accepted as the fixed fee. Should the scope of the work be altered, it will be necessary to adjust the fixed fee.

Such adjustments create problems. Should it be decided to omit repair work and substitute reinstatement combined with improvements, cost comparisons are confused by a multitude of variables. A notional assessment of the value of both the omitted and substituted work, based on the methods used in calculating the original fee, offers the most satisfactory solution.

Standard conditions for civil engineering cost reimbursement contracts do not exist. Fortunately the J.C.T. standard form for the prime cost fixed fee contracts is suitable either in its original state, or with amendments for use as a guide if it is decided to draft a special set of conditions.

Hybrid Contracts

Hybrid forms of contracts are in existence. These have been designed to meet the special requirements of certain classes of work, or have been drafted to suit the needs of a particular promoter or contractor. One of the best known is the target or value cost contract which combines the principle of the cost plus percentage and schedule contracts. A target cost will be obtained either by preparing and pricing approximate quantities, or by taking a value based on one of the recognized methods of approximate estimating. This target, which includes the estimated net cost and the contractor's fee, will be used as the contract sum. Either a schedule of rates or priced bill of quantities will be a contract document. During the progress of the contract, the work will be measured and valued in accordance with the contract rates, and at the same time a cost account will be kept. When the time for settlement arrives the final measured cost and the cost plus the percentage fee are agreed and compared; and the difference between the two sums is apportioned between the parties in accordance with a formula that will have been incorporated in the contract conditions. There are many versions of the target contract. An example of one procedure is given below:

Tendering Data   £M

Measured work 54.000
P.C. sums 10.000
Approximate estimate of cost
(excluding profit and overheads) 64.000
Contractor's fee   ⎱ (12½ per cent) 8.000
Preliminary items ⎰
   Target cost £M72.000

Final Account Data   £M

Remeasurement cost 57.600
P.C. sums 12.000
                                                    69.600
Contractor's fee and preliminary items 8.700
Final measured cost 78.300
Contractor's book cost £M 68.800
Fee (12½ per cent) £M 8.600 ....   77.400
   Saving .... £M 0.900

Final Cost to Employer   £M

Final measured cost 78.300
Less half value of saving 0.450
Amount paid to contractor £M77.850

The saving or excess on the measured cost is not always apportioned in this way. The contractor can agree to bear the whole of the excess book cost, and let the employer take the full benefit of any saving. Another alternative is for the employer to pay the final measured cost and receive the saving, or pay the excess, on the adjusted fee. If this method had been used in the example cited above, the final cost to the employer would be as follows:

£M

Final Measured Cost including fee 78.300

Fee on final measured cost
of £M69.600 .... 8.700

Fee on final book cost .... £M8.600 .100

Amount paid to Contractor £M78.200

The target contract transfers part of the risk which would normally be borne by the contractor carrying out a measured contract to the employer. The extent to which the risk is transferred depends on the method of adjustment at the end of the contract. Some benefit may accrue to the employer because the prices, which will normally contain an element of insurance against these risks, can be reduced in proportion to the decrease in the risks carried by the contractor. The final price to be paid by the employer will always be affected by the instructions he gives during the progress of the work whatever type of contract is used, even though he may often be unaware of the relationship; and in the case of fixed price contacts he may even be sheltered to a limited extent from the complete consequence of his actions. Target contract procedure should ensure that the employer is aware of his interest in the reduction of construction costs, and give him an incentive to reduce site costs regardless of their effect on the measured value of the work. This incentive will not be significant when other factors are of more importance to him than the actual price paid.

There are other hybrid contracts which make the design of

the project an element in the competitive tender. The competing contractors are supplied with a performance specification together with quality standards and sketch drawings. From this information the contractor must prepare in outline his detailed design on which he will then base his quantities. It is usual for the promoter to employ his own consultant to prepare the initial design and adjudicate on the contractors' tenders when they are submitted. Property development schemes sponsored by local authorities usually take a different form. The rival property companies submit their respective schemes and offer competing premiums for a lease of the land. For this purpose a consortium of property companies, architects, and contractors is often formed. This system of competition has been condemned by the J.C.T. It would be out of place in this context to discuss the ethics and social value of such procedures. It is sufficient to say that it has been argued that these are unsatisfactory because of the failure of the employer to settle the order of priority between financial, social and aesthetic values.

In the case of property development the sponsor is seldom interested in the construction cost, and he will not be concerned with the method by which the contractor is paid, but one or other of the fixed price contracts will be utilized to control costs, and safeguard the property company. One form of contract used by both the Central Electricty Generating Board and the British Railways Board is the lump sum contract based on the tenderer's design and quantities; although the quantities do not form part of the contract, the rates in the bills will be used for the pricing of variations. The quantities for this kind of contract are frequently prepared under conditions not conducive to accuracy, and the original tender scheme is more often than not varied considerably. As a result, agreement and settlement of the final account is difficult. While these contracts have the advantage of giving the contractor an opportunity to adapt the design to the most economic construction techniques, there is little else to recommend them. When it is accepted that there is a need for competitive tenders based on the participant's design, the promoter should be advised that the advantages which may accrue from the adoption of this procedure will be largely nullified by variations.

The package deal or turn-key contract is similar, and the bill of quantities may be a contract document. A consortium of professional advisers and a contractor offer to execute a scheme for an all-in price which includes professional fees. This method is popular in Europe and America, and is suited to the needs of the less developed countries in Asia and Africa. These new nations often rely on loans from foreign states or organizations for the financing of their more ambitious schemes, and they find approval is sometimes given more readily to the package contracts. It is generally found that it is in the promoter's interests to employ professional advisers to negotiate with the consortium. Despite its popularity with financing bodies, doubts have been voiced as to whether the employer reaps any extra benefits from this type of contract.

The use of design and build and other forms of package contract has been more widespread in recent years. They are often not suitable for competitive tenders. The promoter will have the advantage that there is no division of responsibility between those specifying the workmanship and material, and those carrying out the work. A document setting out the promoter's requirement is essential; it should not only cover ordinary wear and tear and use of the structure, but also specifically state any factors which will affect the fabric or finishes of the building. Should this not be done either the contractor will successfully disclaim responsibility for some defects, or the repair work and rectification of failure may not be clearly within the terms of the contract. A J.C.T. form "with Contractor Design" is available. With civil engineering projects there has been a tendency to use the services of a consulting engineer before bids for design and construction were made. Package contract is a general term for a growing variety of contracts, and consultants asked to advise on proposals for such schemes should ascertain exactly what is on offer before making an assessment.

Promoters who undertake extensive work which consists of a programme of successive contracts can use the serial contract. Initially, the procedure is the same as for a bill of quantities or schedule contract, and the first contract is the subject of competition. Further contracts are negotiated on the basis of the documents used in the first contract, and all adjustments are made with reference to the original bills. When expensive specialized plant must be bought for the first contract, and it can be utilized for the later ones, the serial contract can effect savings for both parties.

Periodic contracts[1] may be used for work which is both intermittent and recurring. They are most often used for maintenance work, including road surfacing, paving and road repair works. The procedure is for a specification and schedule to be supplied to the competing contractors with the proviso that the successful contractor will be awarded all the work in a given district for a stated period, such as one year. The employer will not give any undertaking as to the quantity of the work he will require carried out during the currency of the contract; on the other hand the contractor will be able to make a reasonable forecast of the amount of work he is likely to be given during the period. The employer can expect to be quoted more favourable rates than he would obtain if each job was the subject of a separate contract; and when maintenance or emergency work must be put in hand speedily, there should be the minimum delay between decision and execution.

Pipes for pipe-lines, steel piles and structural sections, rail-track and tunnel linings are sometimes purchased in bulk by the promoter. Several contracts are then let for the execution of a single scheme, the contractors being paid only for the fixing of the materials supplied by the employer.

The Choice of a Contract

About ten major types of contract have been mentioned, and with the alternative forms of contract available for each type, there are between twenty and thirty forms of contracts from which to choose. The suitability of a particular type and form of contract is often obvious, and the need to make a reasoned evaluation of alternatives does not arise; but on occasions the

[1]The expression term contract is now frequently used.

engineer will have to consider carefully the selection of a form of contract best suited to serve the purpose of the parties. Sometimes even though the choice of contract may appear obvious to the consulting engineer, his client may request to be informed of the reasons which determine its choice in preference to other alternatives. The choice of a contract is often influenced by the preferences of the client or his professional advisers for a type and form of contract with which they are conversant, for the very good reason that the disadvantages of a particular type of form or contract can be offset by familiarity with its function in practice. A change of procedure, however, may have to be considered where special problems arise, or where the form of contract generally used is unsuitable in some major respect.

A chemical firm may wish to develop a new site. The project involves roads, sewers, foundations for heavy plant, single storey sheds, water-cooling and cleaning plant, storage tanks and an office block incorporating a canteen. Assuming the value of the whole is approximately £14,000,000 composed of a mixture of civil engineering and building works combined with the installation of costly processing plant. What advice should be given to the client on the selection of a contract? The client may either require detailed recommendations on which he can base his decision, or he may require his professional adviser to give a decision and support it with a reasoned report. Regardless of how the client phrases his request, it is best to adopt a formal procedure when seeking an answer. A suitable procedure is tabulated below:

1. State the problem.
2. List the possible alternative solutions to the problem.
3. Evaluate each solution.
4. Decide on the most suitable solution, and if necessary incorporate qualifications arising from alternative requirements and circumstances.

The results can be incorporated in a letter or report to the client advising him of the favoured choice. We reproduce the letter written to the principal of the chemical firm considering the project cited above:

Dear Sir,

Re Northtown Scheme

It will be necessary to make a decision on the form of contract to be used before any further progress can be made with this scheme. Our approximate estimate of the different classes of work involved is as follows:

	£
Civil engineering works	3,500,000
Building works	5,600,000
Processing plant	4,900,000
	£14,000,000

The J.C.T. form of contract with quantities would normally be used for building works, and for civil engineering works the I.C.E. form would be used. As your project will include civil engineering works to the value of £3,500,000 and building works to the value of £5,600,000 you have the choice of one of the following procedures:

1. Adopt the I.C.E. form for the whole of the works.
2. Adopt the J.C.T. form with quantities for the whole of the works.
3. Invite separate tenders for both the civil engineering and the building works, and use the I.C.E. form for one, and the J.C.T. form for the other.

As the preponderance of the work will be that normally undertaken by a building contractor, we would advise against the first choice. It would be possible to use the J.C.T. form of contract provided the conditions are amended to permit the engineering sections of the work to be measured in accordance with the civil engineering method of measurements. The second course is the one we would recommend if it is necessary for the project to be phased in sections containing both civil engineering and building works. This course will limit the choice to those contractors capable of dealing with both classes of work. So should you be able to agree a programme that would enable us to plan a sequence of work which resulted in the major part of the building works being consecutive to the civil engineering works we would recommend the third course, which has the advantage of allowing a wider selection in the choice of tenderers, and offers the prospect of a more economic price as a result of having separate contracts for the two categories of work.

The cost of the processing plant represents over one-third of the value of the whole project; and although its installation must be undertaken in sequence with the rest of the work, on the whole the installation will be independent of the constructional work. Therefore we recommend that provision should be made in the bills of quantities for the attendances and builders work in connection with the plant that the contractor will be required to carry out; but that the cost of the plant be excluded from the construction contract, and direct contracts made with the plant manufacturers.

Yours faithfully,
A.N. Consultant.

Although two alternative suggestions are made in the letter, the final preference is made clear to the client once he has made his decision on whether or not to phase the work. Whenever possible the consulting engineer should make clear-cut recommendations, even though he gives information on other procedures; and the final outcome may be dependent on the client's willingness to accept a particular course of action.

One way of resolving the difficulties posed by contracts which contain a heavy element of plant and equipment was mentioned in the example just dealt with. But if it is possible, the plant can be installed after the completion of the constructional works and excluded entirely from the construction contract; and there will be occasions when it will be more effective to make the construction contractor responsible for the plant and equipment, and in these cases prime cost items should be included in the bills. A *prime cost*[1] is a sum included in a contract to cover the cost of either work carried out by a nominated subcontractor or goods obtained from a nominated supplier.

When circumstances compel the combination of both civil engineering and building works in one contract it will usually be wise to make provision for each section of the work to be measured in accordance with the appropriate method of measurement, and contract conditions amended accordingly. The conditions of contract should also be reviewed to ensure that they comply with the requirements of both the building and the civil engineering works. To do this satisfactorily the engineer should be conversant with the clauses contained in both the I.C.E. and J.C.T. forms of contract. Unfortunately, although both the forms have much in common, it is not possible to make a direct clause by clause comparison. Not only are clauses arranged in a different order, but conditions which are self-contained in one contract are fragmented in the other. A summary of the main differences will be found in Appendix 1, together with cross-references. In addition to the conditions both forms contain an appendix which should be completed by the engineer before the tender documents are distributed.

---

[1] I.C.E. contract Cl.58(2).

Form of Tender (Appendix)

The Appendix to the I.C.E. Form of Tender includes the following items. The relevant I.C.E. contract clause numbers are shown in brackets following the description:

1. Amount of bond (if any) (10)   . % of tender total
2. Minimum amount of insurance
    (23(2))   £ . . . .
3. Time for completion (43)
   for the whole of the works and if
   required for sections of the works
   which have to be listed and briefly
   described.   . . . . weeks
4. Liquidated damages for delay (47) £ . . per day/week
   for the whole of the works and if
   required for sections of the works,
   with the reduction in damages as
   defined in Clause 47(2) and the
   damages per day or week for each
   section being stated.
5. Period of maintenance (49 (1))   . . . . weeks
6. Vesting of materials not on site (54(1)
   and 60(1))
   Goods and materials to be listed item
   by item.
7. Standard method of measurement
   adopted in preparation of bills of
   quantities (57)   . . . .
8. Percentage for adjustment of P.C.
   sums (59 A(2)(b) and (5)(c))   . . . . %
9. Percentage of the value of goods
   and materials to be
   included in interim
   certificates (60 (2)(b))   . . . . %
10. Minimum amount of interim
    certificates (60 (2))   £ . . . .

The appendix to the J.C.T. form which is incorporated in the conditions as there is no J.C.T. standard form of tender, uses different wording and omits the first, sixth, seventh, eighth, ninth and tenth items of the I.C.E. appendix, but contains the following additional items referenced to the relevant J.C.T. clauses:

Statutory tax deduction	Cl.31 and 4th recital
Arbitration	Cl.5.1
Percentage to cover professional fees	Cl.22A
Period of delay	Cl.28. 13
Retention percentage	Cl.30.4.1.1
Period of final measurement	Cl.30.6.1.2
Period of issue of final certificate	Cl.30.8
Nominated work for which contractor desires to tender	Cl.35.2
Fluctuations	Cl.37, Cl.38, Cl.39, Cl.40
Formula rules[1]	Cl.40

Differences between Civil Engineering and Building Contracts

The differences between civil engineering contracts and building contracts amount to more than the total effect of the alternative method of measurement employed and the dissimilarity of the contract conditions. The effects of the physical environment on the execution of civil engineering works tend to be more compelling than in the case of building works. The results of contending together against the hazards encountered in deep excavations and marine works tend to produce an underlying sympathy between engineer and engineering contractor. Although architect and builder both consciously endeavour to co-operate, they do not have an opportunity to develop the same type of relationship.

[1]See p. 218.

A United Kingdom government report[1] has recommended that the bodies representing civil engineering and building should consider replacing the various existing forms of contracts with two standard forms, one for civil engineering and the other for building, and eventually superseding these two proposed forms by one common form for all types of construction. While it may be found that practical difficulties will necessitate some modification to the broad recommendation made in the report, it seems likely that it will be possible to take those clauses which already have the same intent in both civil engineering and building contracts, and word them identically.

[1] The Placing and Management of Contracts for Building and Civil Engineering Work (The Banwell Report), H.M.S.O. 1964.

CHAPTER 4

PREPARATION OF THE CONTRACT DOCUMENTS

Pre-contract Programme

The smooth running of any contract will depend in part on the satisfactoriness of the contract documents. This will be influenced by the amount of time allowed for their preparation, and the adequacy of the promoter's instructions. A systematic approach is essential. The initial requirement is the preparation of a pre-contract programme. The contents and sequence of such a programme will vary with the size and type of contract. A generalized programme upon which a specific one could be based is outlined below:

1. Initial consultation with the promoter.
2. Promoter's provisional instructions.
3. Preliminary survey or reconnaissance.
4. Preparation of provisional and alternative designs together with approximate estimates.
5. Submission of alternative proposals with recommendation to the promoter.
6. Promoter's approval of design together with supplementary instructions.
7. Appointment of specialist consultants.
8. Survey and ground investigation.
9. Completion of small-scale working drawings.
10. Cost check.
11. Nominated sub-contractor's estimates.
12. Preparation of specification and detail drawings.

13. Completion of statutory approvals, leases, purchases and wayleaves.
14. Preparation of quantities.
15. Tenders.
16. Acceptance of tenders.

This programme can be set out in the form of a bar chart showing the approximate time needed for each operation. Some items in the programme can be undertaken concurrently, and it is possible to apply the critical path method discussed in a later chapter to the planning of these operations.

At the first meeting between the promoter and the consultant, it is essential that the cost category of the project should be established. These categories can be summarized as follows:

1. A fixed total expenditure is given and the project must be designed and completed within that figure.
2. The total cost limit of the project is not to exceed the product of the unit cost and the total number of units. For instance, the cost of a road or railway could be limited to £6,000 per metre run or a bridge to £36,000 per metre run of span.
3. The cost is related to the income received from the proposed development in comparison with the capital invested.
4. No limitation is set as to cost. An approximate estimate is required solely for budgeting and financial control.

In addition to the identification of the cost category as much other information as is possible should be obtained from the promoter. It is important that the engineer should know whether the requirements will be stated in broad outline, allowing him considerable freedom in solving the design problem, or a precise specification given limiting the design solution to a narrow range of answers. Sometimes the engineer will be called upon to develop in detail schemes already prepared in outline, which for some reason or another have been held in abeyance for some years. The consulting engineer should qualify his acceptance of such a brief with the warning that the passage of time may have made a once adequate scheme obsolescent. In every case it should be made clear that the consulting engineer must reserve his judgement on the promoter's suggestions until he has had time to give them the consideration they deserve. Confirmation in writing of the verbal instructions given at the preliminary meeting should always be obtained. Among other things, these should specify the performance standards and maintenance and user needs, and indicate appearance and amenity requirements, together with all information upon site conditions in the possession of the client. The size, complexity and cost of present day schemes has made a comprehensive written brief essential.

On receipt of these instructions, the consultant should prepare a detailed list of the data he will require to prepare his design. The contents of the list will vary with the function of the project and, with extensive schemes such as motorways, water-supply projects, and docks, there will be a considerable amount of documentary information to classify and absorb. The extent of the pilot survey, reconnaissance, or site investigation carried out before the sketch designs are prepared will depend on the type and nature of the project. At this stage the engineer may use cost planning, the critical path method, and operational research techniques to help him in his task. Reliance on common sense and past experience, coupled with a mistrust of the often expensive and cumbersome apparatus of a formal scientific approach to administration and design, tends to make engineers reluctant to adopt these procedures during the early stages of a project. But the increasing complexity of schemes, and the more exacting standards now demanded, possibly justify the more laborious approach. Often the same solution could be reached more quickly and economically by the application of common sense and reliance on partially intuitive processes. Nevertheless the adoption of deliberate and formal techniques will make it more likely that the best possible solution is the one chosen, and that errors in judgement are detected. When all the information has been collected and the provisional design is completed, it should be submitted to the promoter with an approximate estimate of the cost. Whether alternative designs are submitted will depend to some extent on the nature of the project and the wishes of the promoter.

The approximate estimate should not have too great a margin of error. Fixed limits cannot be stipulated, but the margin of error should not be such as to make the dependability of the estimate derisory.[1] It may not be always feasible to give a dependable figure, and in such cases a forecast of the cost between a lower and a higher figure should be given. Even figures showing a wide difference are preferable to the quotation of a single figure which may have a deceptive appearance of accuracy. It should also be made clear whether the estimate is based on current costs. Subsidiary items and plant installations excluded from the estimate should be expressly mentioned.

Once the promoter's approval of a scheme has been given, his consent in writing to the preparation of the whole of the contract documents should be obtained; and this must be the very latest stage at which the appointment of specialist consultants is made. On large schemes they should be appointed for consultation before the preparation of the sketch designs. The appointment should make clear the demarcation of duties and responsibilities; and it is as well to set forth in writing a procedure for approval of drawings, specifications, and for the acceptance of estimates and transmission of instructions to the contractor and his sub-contractors; the agreement of all consultants to this procedure should be obtained. It should be needless to mention that all decisions and instructions should be communicated to the principal consultant for his approval. Equally important is the distribution of all information and drawings to each of the consultants. Standard forms of appointment exist. The scales of fees and payment to be made if the scheme is abandoned should be clearly stated.

---

[1] Some information on approximate estimates is given in Chapter 5.

Drawings, Specifications, Bills of Quantities

The preparation of the drawings should comply with British Standards.[1] The drawings for any one contract should ideally be of one size. When this is impractical every endeavour should be made to limit the number of sizes to as few as possible. Each drawing should carry in the right-hand bottom corner the name and address of the consultant, the drawing number, scale and title of the drawing. The name or initials of the draughtsman and the checker should also be recorded. A panel on which can be recorded notes of all revisions and amendments with their dates should be incorporated. Methods of numbering drawings vary from office to office. Consistency and an efficient record or reliable file is the primary essential. Every time a drawing is revised, the new index number should have its final reference number or letter changed, otherwise obsolete drawings will be used by one of the people engaged on the scheme. Drawings may be revised by the resident engineer after general issue. Either a further revision drawing must be circulated, or a rider drawing issued.

There are several types of material available for drawing negatives, including linen, plastic film and tracing paper and the type selected will depend on the prospective usage, but care should be taken to prevent tearing and fraying by proper handling and storage and by taping the edges of linen and tracing paper negatives.

To prevent confusion, the number of different scales used on any one drawing should be limited. When two scales are used on one drawing they should be of dissimilar proportions, readily distinguishable by sight. The filling of every possible inch of space with drawings and lettering in confusion is to be avoided. The value of the paper saved is more than offset by the time wasted locating information and deciphering the drawing. When it is necessary to show plans and sections on separate

---

[1] B.S. 308: Part 1 [1972] and B.S. 1192 [1969].

drawings, they should be cross-referenced and section lines clearly indicated.

The engineer who acts as consultant under the direction of an architect will usually be responsible for the design and supervision of the construction of the structural frame. The contract used will normally be a J.C.T. one. It is dangerous to generalize, but it is suggested that the dimensional accuracy and quality of workmanship associated with building works is less than that found with some types of civil engineering work, although the finish will be of a higher standard. Therefore, where practicable, the engineer's design must allow for larger site tolerances than is usual with civil engineering work.

The specification, if there is one, is not a contract document when the J.C.T. quantities contracts are used. In such cases the specification as far as it affects materials and workmanship should be incorporated in the quantities. The specification is a contract document when the I.C.E. contract is used, and it should be prepared in conjunction with the drawings. It is helpful if references to specification clauses are made on the drawings. The specification should be both concise and complete. Each clause should be referenced. Consecutive numbering is not recommended, and it is preferable to give consecutive letter references to the items on each and every page. This facilitates the insertion of additional items at a late stage. The specification must not only describe the workmanship and materials required, but also indicate the position in the works of the various items, if this is not clear from the drawings. Most offices have standard specification clauses which can be used repeatedly; but it is essential that each fresh specification is compiled with care, and each clause scrutinized to ensure that it is appropriate to the contract, and that any further clauses needed are added. For most road construction the Department of Transport's *Specification for Road and Bridge Works* is used.

The bills of quantities must list in an orderly sequence the quantities and description of the items of work to be executed. Each item will include the labour, materials and plant required, unless provision has been made elsewhere in the bill for a separate assessment of one of these components. The quantities are computed from the drawings and the description derived from the specification and the drawings. Missing information discovered during the preparation of the quantities must be added to the drawings and specification, and discrepancies between them must be reconciled. The bills comprise an inventory of the finished work shown on the contract drawings and described in the specification. They must not only cover the cost of all labour, materials, temporary work, plant, overhead charges and profit; but also any other liabilities, obligations and risks which will either form a part of the cost, or represent a potential cost. Work for which the quantities are doubtful, or the descriptions tentative, must be labelled provisional. The Civil Engineering Standard Method of Measurement (C.E.S.M.M.)[1] stipulates the units of measurement to be used in the bills, and groups and classifies the work for separation into items. This standard method of measurement is referred to in Clause 57 of the I.C.E. contract and unless this method has been adopted in the preparation of the bills of quantities, the method used must be expressly stated in the bills and in the appendix to the form of tender.

This C.E.S.M.M. contains eight sections.

1. *Definitions.* Most of these fourteen definitions aim to give the words defined precision combined with generality, and they deserve careful study.
2. *General Principles.* These contain a reminder that the *C.E.S.M.M.* is intended for use only for works of civil engineering construction and in connection with the I.C.E. contract, and that, where appropriate, the *Building S.M.M.* should be used.
3. *Application of the Work Classification.* Work classifications divides civil engineering into 24 main classes of which typical classes are earthworks and *in situ* concrete. The first is Class A general items covering the preliminary and general items of the traditional bill of quantities. Each class comprises up to three divisions which are hierarchal; the first division normally classifies the second division items and third division items are subsidiary to those in

---

[1]New edition to be published in 1985.

the second division. This section should be understood before attempting to interpret the individual works classifications.

4. *Coding and Numbering of Items.* This section is especially useful when it is intended to use a computer in the preparation of the bills. Unfamiliar types of project are more easily billed by old-fashioned long-hand methods.

5. *Preparation of the Bills of Quantities.* Defines the layout of the bills of quantities. It makes provision for a list of principal quantities, which must be stated to be merely for the guidance of tenderers *before* they examine in detail the remainder of the bills and other contractual documents. This section suggests how dayworks should be dealt with in the tender documents, and describes the division of the bill into parts. Each part could contain its own set of work classifications and for the provision of part summaries.

6. *Completion and Pricing of the Bill of Quantities by a Tenderer.* This section contains a clause that a tenderer may insert a lump sum addition or deduction in the grand summary in adjustment of the total of the bill of quantities.

7. *Method-related Charges.* These are of three types.

   (a) Costs of which are not proportional to the quantities of the other items and for which no allowance has been made when pricing the other items.

   (b) "Time-related charge" means a method-related charge for work the cost of which is to be considered as proportional to the length of time taken to execute the work.

   (c) "Fixed-charge" means a method-related charge which is not a time-related charge. Method-related charges are not subject to admeasurement. "Admeasurement" in this usage must mean either remeasurement or adjustment. This is clear from the context, but it will be prudent for the consultant to emphasize this fact in the contract documents. The contractor is not bound to adopt the method stated in the bill description, but he is still entitled to the payment. The amount can only be adjusted if the engineer gives fresh instructions, and then clause 52 of the I.C.E. contract applies.

8. *Work Classifications.* These contain the classifications referred to in section 3, together with notes amplifying classifications, and providing additional rules of measurement.

Risk Borne by the Contractor

Risk is inherent in all commercial transactions. The amount of risk accepted usually bears some relation to the profit expected. A decrease in the certainty of the conclusion will be generally balanced by an increase in the reward expected. Both the I.C.E. contract and the standard method of measurement are drafted with the intention of confining within reasonable limits the risk accepted by an experienced contractor. These intentions may be difficult to fulfil when the risks are abnormal, unless the engineer takes special steps to reduce the element of chance to manageable proportions when preparing the contract documents. The risks involved should be confined to those that can reasonably be foreseen by an experienced contractor. Risk is a necessary element of all fixed price contracts, whether based on accurate quantities or provisional schedules. The task of accurately valuing the cost of the works when tendering, although a test of the contractor's skill, must also involve risk. In addition to the normal risks of management, he will be expected to accept others which, despite recent advances in site investigation techniques, are an inevitable consequence of the uncertainty of site conditions, and the vagaries of the weather. It is suggested that the engineer should endeavour, insofar as it is possible, to put a value on these uncertainties, to ensure that the risk element due to these factors is not more than ten per cent of the estimated contract sum, at the most. As it is probable that the management and operational risks are likely to amount to not less than another ten per cent of the contract sum, it can be seen that the margin of financial safety usually associated with civil engineering contracting is small bearing in mind the fact that the capital involved is probably on average never more than a third of the contract sum. In consequence, when the risks are formidable the tender price will be inflated at the expense of the promoter, and the engineer best serves his client's interests when he makes provision for hazardous operations or liabilities to be paid for in relation to the expenditure actually incurred.

Expenditure upon pumping is a typical example of this type of hazard. Often contractors will be able to make a reliable forecast of the likely pumping requirements; and should their estimates prove wrong, it is probable that circumstances would justify a claim for additional costs within the terms of Clause 12 of the I.C.E. contract. In exceptional cases, the pumping requirements will be so difficult to evaluate that widely ranging amounts would be allowed by contractors of equal experience. It is advisable in such circumstances that arrangements be made for the contractor to be paid for the pumping he actually undertakes, instead of being called upon to gamble heavily on the outcome, and usually pricing high to cover the risk. The inclusion of a schedule of rates in the bills for pumping, together with a provisional sum, not only avoids the need for the contractor to undertake an unfair risk, but ensures that the employer pays only for the pumping that is carried out.

One factor that often gives an engineer a disinclination to transfer the obligation for items of special risk from the contractor to the employer is the knowledge that in the event of unexpected difficulties, it is the skill, care and resource of the contractor that controls the actual expenditure. It is considered, with some justice, that the risk should be borne by the party which has the opportunity to control the expenditure connected with it. This objection can to a certain extent be neutralized by the engineer incorporating instructions in the specification defining the methods to be used when it becomes necessary to expend the provisional sum included in the bills to cover special risks. These instructions should be sufficiently flexible to allow the contractor enough freedom to exercise his skill to its best effect, while providing the engineer with adequate control over the operation.

As a general rule the cost of temporary works shall be covered in the bills of quantities by the rates for the permanent work. It is customary to include in the preliminary bills comprehensive items describing the general nature of the temporary works that serve the works as a whole. Whether or not these temporary works are priced as a lump sum in the preliminary bill, or their cost apportioned to the rates for the measured work, is a matter for the contractor. Decision upon the design and types of temporary buildings and gantries required is usually completely within the contractor's control. Hoardings, temporary works, constructional plant and bridges will also be provided in accordance with the contractor's assessment of the needs of the job, although they may be subject to the consent of the engineer. When the engineer decides he must assume control over the design and specification relating to any of the temporary works, consideration should be given to including measured items in the bills of quantities. These items need not necessarily be measured in the same detail, or in the same manner, as those for the permanent works. Probably, comprehensive items fully described, stating the numbers or lengths required, will be all that is needed. The convenience of the estimator is an important consideration. If the cost of the temporary works is high in comparison with the value of the permanent works, even though the engineer is not concerned with their design or construction, it may be advisable to include measured items in the bills for them. Temporary housing on isolated sites, shafts and adits for tunnels, and temporary dams for river works are examples of the kinds of item which are suitable for this treatment. Unlike the items for permanent works and for those temporary works within the engineer's control these items should only be subject to remeasurement when variations in the permanent works make it necessary, because the extent of such works will depend upon the contractor's planning and approach to the execution of the works.

The Preliminary Bill

The preliminary bill should contain the following items:

1. Description of the works – This should be concise, and yet give the contractor all the basic facts.
2. Situation of the site and access – While it will be the contractor's responsibility to acquaint himself with all matters that affect access to the site, this clause should give as much information as is possible about traffic regulations and road conditions.
3. Division of work into sections – This clause will not always be required, but when needed it is important that the promoter's requirements are set out clearly.
4. Abstract of conditions of contract – Only clause headings should be given, but when new clauses are added to the contract, or amendments made to existing clauses, these should be given in full.
5. Appendix to form of tender – This should give all the information required, and when decisions have not yet been made, it should be stated that the insertion is to be agreed later.
6. Stipulation on working hours and conditions, wages, etc. – This clause can be omitted if the clause in the conditions of the contract is sufficient. Sometimes the promoter will require more amplification, and additional regulations. It may also be important to the promoter that preference is given to the employment of local labour, and sometimes the engineer will be told to state the minimum numbers of local workpeople that must be employed.
7. Warranties.
8. Plant, tools and scaffolding – This clause should be comprehensively worded, and yet be in general terms. In addition when it is necessary for specific items to be measured, they should follow this clause in the bill.
9. Hoarding and gantries – This clause could be merged with the previous one, and the same considerations apply.

10. Offices and sheds – This item should be comprehensive and in general terms. Specific requirements peculiar to the contract should be referred to, although this is not mandatory.

11. Welfare, messrooms, drying rooms and latrines – It is good practice to prescribe fairly high minimum standards to which the contractor must adhere. Good site conditions are essential if the best type of workmen is to be recruited and retained.

12. Health and Safety – All design and site staff should be familiar with health and safety at work legislation.

13. Provision of telephones – Sometimes a p.c. sum is included to cover the cost of calls made by the professional advisers' representatives, and telephone facilities for sub-contractors should be described, and the method of charging dealt with. It is usually prudent to make sub-contractors liable for the cost of their own calls.

14. Notice and fees.

15. Setting out.

16. Supervision.

17. Damage to roads. See p. 152.

18. Protection of public service and company property.

19. Indemnities and contractor's responsibility for injury to persons and property.

20. Insurances – This clause would include a provisional sum for the premiums payable in respect of the insurances covering the promoter's risks. See p. 148–149.

21. Definition of terms *provisional sum and p.c. sum.*

22. Cartage, unloading, packing cases.

23. Attendance on sub-contractors – Many attendances and facilities required by sub-contractors are common to all of them, and they can be catalogued in these clauses. Special attendances required by an individual sub-contractor should be described in the item following the p.c. sum for such sub-contractor's work.

24. Payment and certificates.

25. Watching and lighting – Should the promoter or engineer have minimum requirements, and propose to enforce the

employment of watchmen or guards, and demand other security precautions, these should be described in clear terms.

26. Electric light and power for the works – It is advisable to draw the attention of the contractor to the situation when no mains supply will be available at the commencement of the works, even though contractually it is a matter for the contractor to investigate. When it is proposed to supply power from the promoter's mains or generating plant it should be stated whether or not it will be metered and charged to the contractor.

27. Water for the works – The considerations referred to in connection with the previous clause are applicable.

28. Protection of the works.

29. Fossils, coins and antiquities – The contract conditions provide for the payment of the contractor for the removal and preservation of archaeological finds. This clause should give particulars of the procedure for payment. The discovery of important archaeological remains which result in publicity and delay while professional archaeologists investigate the site may be an embarrassment to both contractor and promoter. Unless the State makes some financial recompense for the losses involved, it can hardly be expected that such discoveries will be treated other than as a hardship.

30. Remeasurement and variations.

31. Daywork accounts.

32. Samples and testing materials and workmanship – p.c. sums should be included for laboratory tests.

33. Temporary roads, ramps and crossovers.

34. Carting away rubbish and cleaning up.

35. Advertising and signboards.

36. Fluctuations.

37. Work executed and material supplied by the employer and his direct contractors.

38. Trespass of workmen – This clause will only be necessary when the promoter occupies part of the site.

39. Limitation on the hours during which compressors or other noisy machinery may be used.

40. Offices and attendances on the representatives of the professional advisers.

Some of the items listed above will not be needed with every contract, and additional items may sometimes be wanted.

Dayworks

The I.C.E. contract offers the alternatives of a provision of a daywork schedule in the bills of quantities, or the use of *The Federation of Civil Engineering Contractors' Schedules of Dayworks* carried out incidental to contract work. It is preferable to incorporate a schedule in the bills, and an example is given below:

Schedule of Daywork Rates

The contractor will not be paid for any work as daywork unless before starting he has obtained the written order of the engineer.

Only time on the actual work will be allowed, and the contractor must make a return in duplicate each day giving full details of the labour, plant and materials used on daywork. The resident engineer will sign these accounts if correct, or when agreed, and return one copy to the contractor. The return shall list the names and occupations and hours spent on daywork of all workmen employed on such work together with the description and quantity of all materials and plant used. The contractor shall submit a priced statement of the labour, plant and materials used to the resident engineer at the end of each month.

The rates for labour are to include for the provision and use of ordinary tools, plant, staging, scaffolding, and artificial lighting required, and all establishment charges, supervision and profit.

The rates for labour are to include for travelling time, expenses, holidays with pay contributions, national insurance contributions, and any other emoluments received by the workmen.

The time of gangers or charge hands (i.e. men actually working with their hands) will be paid for; but the time of foremen and walking gangers will not be paid for directly as they are considered to be supervisory.

Should the contractor employ workmen of a more highly paid trade or grade than the resident engineer considers necessary for the work ordered, payment will be made only at the rates considered necessary for such work. Mates or labourers attending on craftsmen will be paid only for the actual time assisting and in such numbers as are approved by the resident engineer.

The rates for plant are to apply only to plant which the contractor may have brought upon the site to carry out the main contract work, and are to include for wear and tear, depreciation, repairs, and all other costs and charges. The rates for mechanically operated plant are in addition to include for operator, attendants, fuel and consumable stores. Only the actual hours worked will be paid for.

Temporary works, staging, wagons, and tracks will only be paid for when used exclusively for the dayworks.

All prices for materials are to include for delivery to the site, and profit, etc.

All rates and prices quoted for daywork must bear a reasonable relation to the rates and prices given elsewhere in the bills of quantities, and will be considered in conjunction therewith:

LABOUR

Unit	Description	Rate
Hours	Labourer or mate (any trade)	
"	Ganger	
"	Timberman	
"	Piling operative	
"	Crane driver	
"	Banksman	

Unit	Description	Rate
Hours	Concrete finisher	
"	Carpenter	
"	Fitter	
"	Steel fixer	
"	Pump attendant (day)	
"	Pump attendant (night)	
"	Diver, including suit, gear pumps and telephone	
"	Attendant on diver	
"	Boatman	

PLANT

Unit	Description	Rate
Hours	38 mm diameter submersible electric pump, including 30 m of hose	
"	50 mm ditto	
"	75 mm ditto	
"	30 m of additional hose	
"	Pneumatic tool and air supply (excluding operator)	
"	Crane not exceeding 6.5 tonnes lifting capacity	
"	Crane exceeding 6.5 tonnes and not exceeding 12.5 tonnes lifting capacity	
"	300 litres capacity concrete mixer including hopper	
"	Diving boat	
"	Pulling boat	
"	Pile-driving plant on pontoon or staging complete with frame, fuel, attendant and operator	

MATERIALS

Unit	Description	Rate
m^3	Sand	
m^3	Coarse aggregate	

Unit	Description	Rate
Tonnes	Portland cement	
"	Rapid hardening cement	
"	6 mm diameter mild steel rods	
"	12 mm ditto	
"	18 mm ditto	
"	25 mm ditto	
"	32 mm ditto	
m^3	Hardcore	
m^2	12 mm plywood	
m^3	Shuttering timber	

Working Rule Agreements

The engineer should have some knowledge of the industry's working rule agreements before he compiles a daywork schedule. The working rule agreement for the civil engineering industry is published and sponsored by the Civil Engineering Construction Conciliation Board for Great Britain. Its members are representatives of the Federation of Civil Engineering Contractors and the various trade unions who represent the operatives usually employed on a civil engineering project. This agreement stipulates the official wage rates payable to the various grades and trades employed including plus rates for work requiring additional skill or resulting in discomfort. Concrete levellers receive extra money, while men working in enclosed active foul sewers receive an additional 15p per hour. There are graded payments for working at heights on detached *tower-like structures*, or for working at great heights exposed to the weather. Working hours are also prescribed and any hours worked after the end of the agreed working day or at weekends must be paid for at higher rates. The payments vary according to the number of overtime hours worked. Special rates are applicable to night, tidal work, and shift work. There are rules for the payment of wages, for hours lost due to inclement weather, and a guaranteed minimum wage is also prescribed. Rates and the number of hours in the working week are varied from time to time. The engineer should consult the current working agreement when he requires information. Other matters with which this agreement is concerned are travelling and subsistence allowances, welfare, holidays, tea breaks and the settlement of disputes between employers and their workmen. The building industry has a similar working rule. At the present time the working rules for the two industries differ in some important respects. This can cause administrative problems on sites where building and civil engineering work are carried out in conjunction with each other. It is to be hoped that uniformity between the two agreements will be obtained one day because it will be to the advantage of all.

Estimates of Nominated Sub-contractors

The appointment of a nominated sub-contractor inevitably complicates the situation between the parties to the contract, and where possible any specialist work should be measured and made the responsibility of the general contractor. Where an engineer or an architect needs to keep firm control over the selection of the sub-contractor, it is possible to list in the bills of quantities the names of approved specialist firms who will be suitable as domestic sub-contractors to carry out these works. The J.C.T. 80 contract stipulates that at least three firms should be named, and although this procedure is not referred to in the I.C.E. contract, there should be no objection to its use. When occasions occur where only a single firm will be equipped to carry out this specialist work it may not be considered appropriate to list a single firm as a specified domestic sub-contractor. Yet, providing the probability of the tenderers names becoming known to each other is not considered objectionable, it may be sensible to list the name of a single specified sub-contractor, and so avoid problems in matching the sub-contractor's programme to that of the successful tenderer, and unwelcome delays occurring in the placing of the sub-contract order. Before this step is taken an undertaking from each sub-contractor should be obtained that he will conform with the I.C.E. or J.C.T. conditions; should he refuse to do so, he should not be listed. Usually it is possible to name three firms, and the listing of a single firm should not be used as a stratagem to avoid complying with the intent of J.C.T. 80.

Estimates should have been obtained from nominated sub-contractors before the bills of quantities are completed. The importance of doing so will depend upon the extent to which the specialist work will affect the design and detailing of the whole scheme. An estimate for asphalt work may be relatively unimportant, but those for a proprietary system of piling or pre-stressed concrete construction may be of critical importance. Preferably competitive tenders should have been obtained for these p.c. sums, and a provisional selection of a sub-contractor made. The p.c. sum included in the quantities should be rounded off to an even figure, a little above the amount of the estimate, or increased by a reasonable amount to allow for contingencies. Occasionally the p.c. sum must be based on an approximate estimate, but this is to be avoided whenever possible.

The nomination provisions are dealt with in Clause 59 of the I.C.E. contract; Clause 35 of the J.C.T. 80 contract gives more detailed procedures for nomination. There are two forms of J.C.T. sub-contract. If a detailed tender procedure is followed NSC/4 is used. Where a simpler tender procedure is needed NSC/4A is used. The bills should include as much information as possible about programme, shop-drawings and all other relevant matters to help the tenderers.

An invitation for a tender from sub-contractors should contain the following information:

1. Forms of sub-contract and main contract.
2. Whether tender is to be for a fixed price or is on a fluctuating basis, and the method of assessing fluctuations.
3. Facilities to be provided by the main contractor including particulars of any materials provided such as sand and cement used for fixing pre-cast units, and power to be provided for plant; exclusion of the power for heavy plant such as cranes should be explicitly stated.
4. Cash discount to be included for the main contractor.

5. Whether or not remeasurement of the work is required on completion.
6. Conditions relating to payment and retention.
7. Extent of insurance cover required.
8. Preliminary programme including periods required for preparation of shop-drawings, execution of shop works, and execution of site works.
9. Notice required before commencement on site.

A schedule of quantities, specification and drawings should be provided. But if no schedule of quantities is provided, it should be made clear whether the sub-contractor will be required to submit his own priced schedules of quantities, or a lump sum price. The sub-contractor should also be requested to allow for compliance with the main contractor's programme, and for a reasonable number of visits to the site. It may be difficult for a sub-contractor to forecast the main contractor's requirements; and some consultants prefer to obtain provisional estimates at the pre-tender stage, and call for firm estimates after the appointment of the main contractor, and thus enable the sub-contractor to obtain information about starting and finishing dates, and other matters affecting cost, from the main contractor, before he prepares his estimate.

It is generally agreed that the number of p.c. items should be reduced to the minimum compatible with the satisfactory execution of the work at an economic price. Not all contractors are equally equipped to carry out specialist works. One firm may be able to carry out an electrical installation, and another will be equipped to erect structural steelwork; both are suitable as main contractors. The solution is to include those contractors on the main tender list capable of carrying out specialist works in the invitations for p.c. tenders which are appropriate.

Sureties and Performance Bonds

A clause in the I.C.E. contract requires the contractor to provide sureties who will guarantee his performance of the contract in a sum not exceeding 10 per cent of the tender sum if the tender contains such an undertaking. Suitable terms for such an undertaking are contained in the Form of Bond at the end of the I.C.E. contract. Sometimes the requirement for a bond is omitted from the contract. This should not be done without the promoter's approval. The omission of a bond will mean that careful consideration must be given to fixing retention percentages and to the amount of the limit of retention. The limit of retention should be higher when the contract makes no provision for a bond which guarantees performance. In exceptional cases or where retention is not held, the bond should be in a sum for a percentage greater than that called for by the standard conditions. Bonds should always be under seal. Responsible opinion is in favour of limiting the use of these bonds to contracts which are obtained in open tender.

Banks and insurance companies usually provide bonds. The cost of the bond will vary with the reputation of the contractor, and the risk associated with the work. The availability of money will also influence the charges made by sureties for a bond. The law relating to guarantees and sureties is complex. It is therefore vital that the bond should be worded so as to give the promoter complete cover. Bonds can be made ineffective for a number of reasons. The first is concealment of material facts which might have influenced the surety at the time the bond was given, when the circumstances are such as would not be expected to exist between the parties; for instance, when it is not disclosed that the surveyor or engineer of a third party will be responsible for supervision and certification. The failure of the promoter to carry out the duties imposed on him by the contract will also make the bond ineffective; e.g., failure to insure the works when he has agreed to do so and failure of the employer's agents to supervise may in some circumstances bar the employer from recovering the guaranteed sum. Extensive variations to the contract may also invalidate the bond. The form of bond attached to the I.C.E. contract does explicitly provide for the bond to be effective despite alteration in the terms of the contract, variations, an increase in the extent of the work, or the waiving of contractual rights. The engineer called upon to satisfy the employer about the terms of a bond should seek expert guidance before giving an opinion.

The employer can only recover the amount of damages proved. If this is less than the total amount of the bond and further damages are proved, the residue can be used to meet a subsequent claim. The J.C.T. contracts do not mention sureties, although local authorities will occasionally require a bond when using the J.C.T. contract. The tender documents should provide for a guarantee in these cases, and a clause should be added to the contract. A single bank or insurance company may be a sufficient surety. It is not customary for individuals to act as sureties, but if they do, it is wise to have not less than two as guarantors, and they must be able to provide sufficient security. Maintenance bonds which provide a guarantee to make good defects during the maintenance period are occasionally called for. Retention money will normally provide sufficient security, and their use should be given consideration only in exceptional circumstances.

Unit Rates

Every engineer should have some knowledge of the methods used by contractors when pricing bills of quantities. The components of a rate for a typical bill item will be materials, labour and plant. A percentage for profit and overheads will normally be added to the value of each component. A representative build-up for a single example is given below:

Cost of supplying and fixing 1 tonne of 25 mm diameter mild steel rods reinforcement in walls

Materials	£	£
1.1 tonnes of R25 mild steel reinforcement at £450 per tonne (including waste) ...	495.00	
1 kg galvanised tying wire at 50p per kg.	.50	
2 spacer blocks at 25p	.50	
continued	£496.00	

continued	£496.00	
Add 10 per cent for profit and overheads	49.60	545.60
Labour		
9 hr steel fixer at £5.00	45.00	
9 hr labourer at £4.75	42.75	
	87.75	
Add 20 per cent for profit and overheads	17.55	105.30
Plant		
Power-operated bar-bending machine		
¼hr @ £6.00	1.50	
Add 10 per cent for profit and overheads	.15	1.65
Cost of 1 tonne R25 diameter mild steel reinforcement		£652.55

Sometimes special additional items must be allowed for in the price. For instance, in the above example nothing has been allowed in the rate for the cost of preparing bar-bending schedules and marking plans. Another £50 or thereabouts should be added to the rate for the cost of their preparation and printing. These will usually be prepared by the consultant. The cost of providing and maintaining a weatherproof shed to house the bar-bending plant is allowed for in the percentage addition. It could equally well have been excluded, and included in the amount for plant given in the preliminary bill. The price for materials should be based on a manufacturer's or merchant's quotation, and if the cost of delivery is not already included in the price it must be added. Materials must be unloaded, stacked, and distributed, and the cost involved can either be added to the unit cost of the material, as in the example given above, or allowed for in the labour cost. A percentage of waste and loss is inevitable with most materials and this must be allowed for. Ten per cent has been allowed for in the above example; sometimes the wastage on reinforcement rods can be much more.

The hourly rate of operatives should be adjusted to cover the *oncosts* or the percentage of profit and overheads must allow for them. *Oncosts* is a collective term for the miscellaneous charges over and above the net hourly trade union rate of pay for an operative that must be paid by the employer. The national insurance and holiday stamp contributions of the employer, and the cost to the employer of guaranteed time and workmen's compensation are oncosts. In addition the oncosts should provide for a proportion of payments at overtime rates, and extra payments that are necessary to attract operatives in times of labour scarcity. It is not usual for an allowance to be made for incentive payments, as the time included in the calculation will usually be the target hours. The incentive bonus received by the operative should represent the value of the time saved in relation to the time allowed in the original price build-up, although some contractors deduct a proportion of this saving to pay for the cost of operating a bonus scheme.

The cost of mechanical plant can either be based on a hire charge or upon the running, maintenance and capital cost of plant owned by the contractor. There are several methods of obtaining the latter cost, the simplest being the straight line method, a formula for which is given below:

$$\frac{I}{aw} + \frac{M}{w} + f = x,$$

where I = initial cost
a = life of plant expressed in years
w = average number of hours worked per year
M = annual charge for maintenance and renewals
f = hourly fuel and lubrication cost
x = cost per working hour

An example for a piece of plant with a life of 4 years costing £10,000 and working each year on an average for 1000 hours is given overleaf:

$$\frac{10\,000}{4 \times 1000} + \frac{10\,000}{1000} + 1$$

$$= 2.5 + 10 + 1$$
$$= £13.50 \text{ per hour}$$

The likely number of hours worked per year by an item of plant must be based on historic costs. It is inevitable that plant will be idle for a significant proportion of its stay on any site. Plant may also be standing unproductive in the contractor's yard for short or long periods. Reducing to a minimum the proportion of idle time in the life of an item of plant is normally an important management objective.

CHAPTER 5

COST

Before the design and construction of any civil engineering project is completed, the following essential steps have to be taken.

1. The promoter or client must make a decision as to his precise requirements and must brief the engineer or designer.
2. The engineer must carry out a preliminary investigation of the various technical means of meeting the client's requirements and must produce sketch plans of several solutions.
3. The engineer, either from his own experience or with the assistance of a quantity surveyor, must produce an approximate estimate for each of the solutions.
4. The client must decide which solution he selects, and must also agree that he desires the engineer to proceed with the detailed design. He will also expect the engineer to adopt a method of cost control of the design process to ensure that the approximate estimate, which has now become a budget, is not exceeded.
5. (a) If the project is to be carried out by competitive tender, the engineer will obtain a check on his approximate estimate when tenders are received. He will, however, as the project proceeds, have to compare continuously the payments due under the terms of the contract to the contractor against the relevant items of budget, and will have to inform the client of any changes in anticipated total expenditure. The responsibility for

carrying out the project at the contract price and conditions will have been passed to the contractor.

5. (b) If the project is to be carried out on a prime cost or target basis, continuous cost control of the actual construction process will have to be carried out, comparing actual construction costs against the appropriate items in the budget. Again, any changes in anticipated total expenditure must be notified to the client. If the actual costs are higher than anticipated, it may be possible to change the method or rate of construction to bring the project back within the budget.

Approximate Estimates

Approximate estimates have to be produced before formal bills of quantities are produced, and the system usually adopted initially is to take off approximate quantities and then from previous experience of the prices charged to the promoter (or costs incurred by the promoter) for similar items the total approximate estimate can be arrived at. Various tables are published giving current costs for the most typical items regularly encountered in civil engineering works. The tables published every three months in the magazine *Civil Engineering and Public Works Review* provide a quick way of obtaining a rough approximate estimate for any project, and will be quite adequate for deciding which of the preliminary sketch plans should be presented to the promoter.

This type of approximate estimate is known as a forecast cost estimate (single purpose estimate) and provides an assessment of a single sketch design. The preparation of forecast cost estimates for two or three different sketch designs will provide an indication of which design will be most economic, but will not reveal the reasons why. Comparative cost estimates (dual purpose estimates), which give the approximate cost of each element in the structure, and enable any given design to be adapted to reduce the cost of extravagant elements in the least costly design, are used to aid cost control on building projects.

This method is not so easily applied to civil engineering works, where normally the alternative sketch designs often offer two fundamentally different solutions which are only comparable as a whole. Water supply and sewerage schemes may involve the choice between a deep tunnelled section, or sub-surface pipe lines and pumping station. The apparent difference in cost between the two schemes would be misleading as maintenance and running costs must be taken into account to obtain a true comparison.

The question of deciding whether to reduce the running costs of a railway line by keeping gradients to a minimum and incurring greater capital costs because of the extra costs of earthworks is typical of the interaction between capital cost, running costs and maintenance costs. Caution is needed in interpreting these figures, as variables, such as the amount of traffic and the depreciation in money, complicate the choice.

Very large civil engineering projects, such as dams, long roadways and harbours, present special problems for approximate estimates; it will usually be more accurate to decide on the method and period of construction, numbers of men and machines and amounts of materials, and build up to a total estimate. This process inevitably takes longer, but there can be such enormous variations in the output of men and machines under different conditions that in all cases where very large quantities of one item are involved, it is prudent to adopt this method.

Large scale earthworks, such as the digging of a 30 mile canal, are typical examples. The rated output of a certain excavating machine according to the maker's catalogue may be, say, 80 m^3 per hour under normal weather conditions and in clay. Manufacturers of earth-moving equipment nearly always quote optimistic figures for the performance of their machines, and after due allowance has been made for this, the estimator must make an intelligent estimate of the condition the ground will be in at the time of year when the works will be carried out. It may well be that if the works are to be carried out in winter, an output of only 40 m^3 per hour would in fact be obtained, i.e. only half of the rated output. This, of course, would have the effect of multiplying by two the cost of excavation. This example has been chosen to show the enormous variation in actual costs which can occur if work is carried out at different times of the year. In arriving at an approximate estimate, it is always prudent to err on the pessimistic side.

Under the normal weather conditions experienced in Great Britain one week's output of either plant or men will normally take the following periods in winter:[1]

	Under Building Regulations	Under Civil Engineering Regulations
Excavation on machine working ...	1.5 weeks	1.8 weeks
External finishings ...	1.3 "	1.6 "
Internal finishings (before "heat-on") ...	1.1 "	1.3 "
Internal finishings (after "heat-on") ...	1.0 "	1.2 "

The difference in output between work carried out under building regulations and civil enginering regulations is due to the fact that in Great Britain a building contractor usually works a constant number of hours throughout the year, whereas a civil engineering contractor works shorter hours in the winter months. Clearly, similar factors to this would prevail in other parts of the world, and it is most important that these variations in output at different times of the year are taken into account when estimates are being prepared.

Actual working time usually requires other corrections also before calendar times can be obtained. The incidence of public holidays, the time of year when the bulk of labour takes its annual holiday and even weekends must be allowed for.

---

[1] November until March. The multipliers are related to one week during the rest of the year.

Critical Path Method

For over fifty years construction projects which are essentially *one off* (i.e., not likely to be repeated) in nature have been scheduled on Gantt or bar charts. Although the bar chart is still a useful tool for small projects, it is very limited for the scheduling of large projects, as it does not adequately show all the complex interactions and precedence relationships which exist among the project events. It is being rapidly succeeded by a network scheduling technique known as *Critical Path Method*. This is a way of graphically representing the sequences of operations which constitute a complete project. The inter-dependent operations, which take the longest time to perform and are therefore critical and govern the duration of the whole project, are immediately apparent.

To illustrate the Critical Path Method, the Gantt bar chart and the corresponding network schedule have been drawn for the same operation and to the same time scale in Figs. 1 and 2.

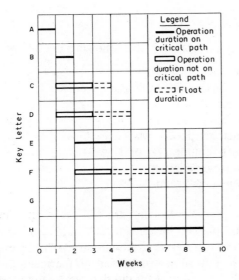

FIG. 1   Gantt bar chart

Network schedule
drawn to time scale

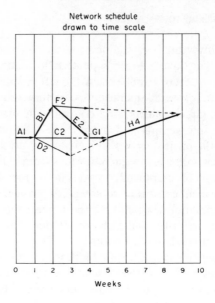

Fig. 2

The key letters represent the following operations:

A. Set out site.
B. Obtain consent for temporary works.
C. Test pile.
D. Obtain reinforcement.
E. Construct temporary works, east wall.
F. Construct temporary works, west wall.
G. Commence pile group.
H. Complete pile group.

The critical path on the network schedule is shown in a heavy black line and consists of operations A1, B1, E2, G1 and H4. These are the critical operations for this particular project, and the time taken to carry them out determines the total duration of the project, i.e., nine weeks. The numbers after the letters on the network schedule are the durations of the individual operations in weeks.

The float duration shown dotted on the Gantt chart is the amount of spare time available after the completion of an operation until the next operation can commence. The operation can, in fact, be carried out at any time within the float period.

Methods based on network techniques, other than the "arrow" diagram shown, have been developed. Among these are "line of balance" and precedence diagrams. Further information on all these techniques may be found in the books mentioned in the bibliography.

Any project consists of so many jobs (or activities). All activities cost something and the cost of the project varies with the time taken to do the activities. These three items, activities, cost, and time, are always interrelated. To perform an activity in less time than the optimum costs more. Equally, to perform an activity in more time than the optimum costs more. The relationship is best shown diagrammatically in Fig. 3.

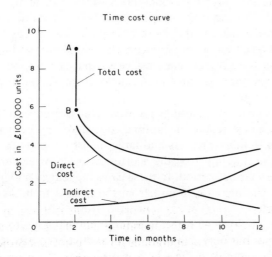

Fig. 3

The total project cost is built up from a simple addition of the direct costs (labour, plant, materials, etc.) and the indirect costs (supervision, head office charges, etc.). Direct costs are high when the period is short and steadily reduce as the period is lengthened, while indirect costs steadily increase with lengthening period. The total project cost curve has therefore a low point which is the optimum time for the contract, combined with the lowest cost. Most operations can be speeded up from the normal time required for performance at normal or least cost. This speeding up adds to the costs as it represents such steps as overtime work, multiple shift operations, larger but less efficient work gangs, and the use of more expensive equipment and methods. Each operation has some practical time limit beyond which it cannot be shortened further. This is referred to as the *crash* time and the corresponding cost is the *crash* cost. If the crash time and cost are worked out for every operation, a point on the project time cost curve "A" known as the *all crash* point is obtained. This represents the shortest possible project time. As the cost is the summation of the crash costs of every operation, it is therefore the highest possible cost. Generally, however, it is possible to achieve the shortest project time by speeding up only those operations which are on the critical path. There is no point in speeding up those operations which are non-critical, for this merely results in an increase in cost without a corresponding reduction in overall project time. The point on the project time cost curve that corresponds to the lowest cost for crash time performance is shown by the point B on the diagram.

Most civil engineering projects are carried out in the minimum cost region of the time cost curve, but occasions do arise on military projects and large industrial schemes, where either the time must be the shortest possible or else the time must be an exact period. In these cases the critical path method enables the increase in cost from the normal to be kept to a minimum.

Each activity in a project is important in that it has to be done sometime, but only a limited number actually control the time needed to complete the whole project. These are the critical activities – critical because a delay in any one of them affects all the others following, with a consequent delay in the completion of the project as a whole. All the other activities are non-critical, because they have some spare time or *float*. However, if the float associated with a non-critical activity is used up, it immediately becomes critical.

Once the critical path has been determined, it is advisable to examine the activities composing it in greater detail to ensure that the time estimates are as accurate as possible. It is possible that either by revising the time estimates, or else by deciding to speed up certain activities on the critical path, the whole project period may be reduced. It may also happen that when the first critical path is shortened, then a second critical path is formed, which in turn must be examined.

The use of the critical path method is by no means confined to the actual physical construction operations on site; it should also be used for controlling the design process, obtaining client's approval, arranging finance, etc. Although the concept of critical path is very simple and the arithmetic involved is also elementary, the process of building up a network becomes very tedious if more than 150 activities are involved in a project. For projects of more than 150 activities, it is more convenient to use a computer, and this also has the added advantage of speed. Most of the large computer centres have programmes already in existence for the preparation of critical path schedules and can give much valuable advice on the method of presenting the information to them.

When late instructions or extra works orders are issued on a project, there is very often a corresponding effect (usually an increase) on project time and cost. The equitable settlement of these contractual claims has always been very difficult, but the application of the critical path method to the problem makes for a much fairer solution. Not only does the critical path method provide the mechanics for determining all of the operations affected by a given change as well as the effect on project duration, but it also provides the mechanics for determining the least cost to compress project time back to its original date if this is necessary.

Risks of all sorts are inevitably associated with civil engineering projects and very large expenditure is incurred by the client to minimize the effects of these risks. A more rational approach to the decisions regarding expenditure to lessen risks is possible since the advent of network scheduling. For example, when a dam is built it is normal to construct a small dam on the upstream side of the main dam, so that the main construction can be carried out in the dry. The higher this temporary dam is, the more it will cost; but at the same time the risk of damage to the permanent works, and possibly also to towns further downstream, would be lessened. From an examination of river levels over a period of years, the probability of the river level reaching the top of the temporary dam at various dates could be worked out. The cost of the resulting damage, should the river go over the top, could be estimated. The probability multiplied by the cost would indicate the *cost of risk* and the critical path network could provide the means for computing the cost of speeding up the critical operations to decrease this risk cost.

Mention has been made before of the desirability of reducing idle time for an item of plant. The design engineer can assist the contractor by considering how the work shown on the drawings and described in the specification will be actually carried out. For instance, when pre-cast units must be lifted into position, it will aid the contractor if the weight of unit is confined to a narrow range, so that neither a powerful crane is employed in lifting small loads, nor are two cranes used when one would have sufficed but for the wide difference in the weights of the concrete units. The network scheduling technique is also capable of revealing to the engineer those elements in his design which add disproportionately to the contract time. This has particular relevance to operations which must be sequential because of safety or other considerations. Sequential operations, of course, cannot be dispensed with. Nevertheless it is sometimes possible for the design to be adapted so that these sequential operations can be arranged to take place without delaying the progress of the bulk of the work.

One of the elements in the cost of a project is the cost of the money needed to finance its execution. Whether this cost is incurred in paying interest on money borrowed, either by a contractor or a promoter, or to the loss of potential profits on capital used for the project, a method of reducing these financing costs is to plan the works so that sections can be completed and put into gainful use before the completion of the whole scheme. Care must be taken to ensure that the sectionalization of the works does not result in construction costs increasing to an extent which exceeds any savings obtained on the interest charges or their capital equivalent.

Despite all the obvious advantages of critical path planning it must be remembered that to minimize cost every member of the client, design and construction team should understand the programme. Field staff often need a date-oriented visual schedule, and for this purpose a bar chart should be developed from the network.

Discounted Cash Flow

Civil engineering projects usually require the expenditure of considerable sums of money in the hope of a future profit. Discounted cash flow is a forecasting technique which endeavours to improve the evaluation of the profitability of a scheme and to grade rival projects in an order of likely profitability. This technique is sometimes called cost-benefit analysis, but cost-benefit analysis is an attempt to assess benefits to the community which are not directly expressible in money terms. Therefore the two terms are not strictly interchangeable.

The use of discounted cash flow techniques, hereafter called D.C.F., are not held universally in high regard, and have offered fertile grounds for differences of opinion. Cost-benefit analysis has provoked even stronger clashes of viewpoint because it deals not only with the intangible but also with matters which present problems to government and community at all levels.

An engineer will find it useful to have an outline knowledge of D.C.F. which is likely to be used by his client or his client's investment advisers. As there are many pitfalls for the unwary it should be borne in mind that a superficial knowledge of the terminology and procedures will only enable him to understand his client's requests for data for his specialist financial advisers. It will not give him competence to use this technique unassisted.

The money used to finance a construction project is either borrowed or taken from invested funds. In the first case interest has to be made on the loan, in the latter case interest paid on the funds previously invested is lost, and the interest is assumed to compound each year. These costs are offset eventually by the income from the construction project after deducting capital and running costs. D.C.F. allows one to relate the forecast of income and expenditure arising from a project to the income received from investment, whether by depositing the money in a bank or from some more adventurous use. This aim is achieved by relating the expenditure and income spread over a number of years to a base year value. Usually the first year of the project is chosen as the base year. In the example which follows, the effects of taxation and inflation are ignored, partly because of the need for simplicity in exemplification, and partly because the possible effect of future taxation and inflation is difficult even for the expert to cope with.

Year	Costs £	Benefits £
0	711,612	
1	2,000,000	
2	4,000,000	
3	—	2,000,000
4	—	3,600,000
5	—	3,600,000

Figure 4 shows the values graphically.

It is a convention to take the money spent in year 0 as being spent at the beginning of year 1, and therefore not subject to discounting. The sums for the other years are brought to the same value (known as present value) as the initial investment by the following formula:

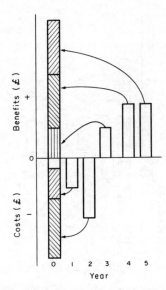

Fɪɢ. 4. Diagram showing costs and benefits (blank boxes) for each year transformed to year zero (hatched boxes).

$$\text{Present value of future sum} = \frac{\text{Future sum}}{(1+r)^n}$$

where r is the discount rate and n is the number of years the discount rate has been in operation.

The calculation for the present values for the above example is as follows:

$$-£711,612 + \left(\frac{-£2,000,000}{1.125}\right) + \left(\frac{-£4,000,000}{1.2656}\right)$$

$$+ \left(\frac{£2,000,000}{1.4238}\right) + \left(\frac{£3,600,000}{1.6018}\right) + \left(\frac{£3,600,000}{1.8020}\right)$$

$$= -£711,612 - £1,777,776 - £3,160,556$$

$$+ £1,404,692 + £2,247,472 + £1,997,780$$

$$= 0.$$

ACE–E

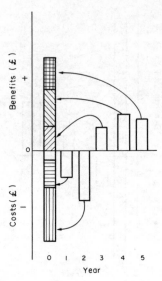

FIG. 5. Diagram showing costs and benefits (plain boxes) for each year transformed to year zero (hatched boxes).

Figure 5 shows the discounted value graphically.

The final value is called the present worth, and in this case is zero because after five years at an interest rate of 12½ per cent the values of the income and expenditure are equal. All future discounted benefits (which are defined as net returns after deducting costs and allowing for the compounding of the interest rate) will represent profits additional to those which could have been obtained if the funds had been earning 12½ per cent interest.

The percentage at which the return on the scheme is zero is known as the internal rate of return. If at a given interest rate the scheme shows a loss, obviously it is not profitable; a scheme with the highest return above zero is, obviously – all matters being equal – the most desirable.

The internal rate of return may have more than one value, and the profitability of a scheme may be confined between an upper and lower bound interest rate. For instance, a scheme may be profitable above a rate of 10 per cent and below a rate of 15 per cent, but not at rates below 10 per cent or exceeding 15 per cent.

D.C.F. can also be used to evaluate the relative merits of increasing the initial capital cost so as to reduce maintenance work or reducing capital costs and so increasing maintenance costs.

These comparisons could be misleading and must be subject to careful criticism and tests before submission to a client. A study of life cycle costs which will include running and maintenance costs during the life of a project cannot have a similar reliability to capital cost forecasts which are themselves difficult to predict in times of accelerating change and for pioneer structures. Despite these difficulties these procedures are essential tools in assessing the financial viability of a scheme, and provide useful aids to monitoring costs during the development of the design and construction.

It is often important to make adjustments for inflation rates which when taken into the calculations will indicate an improved return, and deflation has the opposite effect. For the sake of simplicity it is usually assumed that inflationary and deflationary trends will affect all sectors of the market in much the same way. Needless to say, things do not occur in so neat a manner. Construction costs may suffer from inflationary rises while the returns from the project are reduced by deflation. Fortunately such unhappy combinations are relatively infrequent, and the consultant, while forecasting the trend in construction costs must rely on his client to provide the information on the returns he expects from the project and the allowance to be made for inflationary trends, on his sales.

When inflation is taken into account an adjusted discount rate can be calculated. When the interest rate is higher than the rate of inflation then an adjusted discount rate can be obtained as follows:

$$\text{Adjusted discount rate} = \frac{1 + i}{1 + f} - 1$$

i = interest rate $\qquad$ f = inflation rate

In the example given overleaf, if the rate of inflation is assumed to be 10 per cent then the adjusted discount rate will be 2.27 per cent obtained as follows:

$$\frac{1.125}{1.10} - 1 = 2.27 \text{ per cent}$$

When interest rates are below the inflation rate then the formula used to adjust the interest rate is as follows:

$$\text{Adjusted discount rate} \quad = \frac{1 + f}{1 + i} - 1$$

f = inflation rate; $\qquad$ i = interest rate

Applying an inflation rate of 14.75 per cent to our example it is found that the adjusted discount rate will be 2 per cent which is obtained as follows:

$$\frac{1.1475}{1.125} - 1 = 2 \text{ per cent}$$

This present worth is increased and the effective negative discount rate is 1.96 per cent which is found as follows:

$$-\left(1 - \frac{100}{102}\right) = -1.96 \text{ per cent}$$

Tables are not readily available for these negative rates but they can be found as follows:

$$(1 + a)^n = \text{Present value}$$

$$\text{where } a = \text{effective negative rate}$$
$$n = \text{years}$$

When the adjusted rate is negative it must be remembered that the present value factor is no longer a divisor, but becomes a multiplier. Assuming the same costs and benefits as in the above example with an adjusted negative rate of 2 per cent (effective negative rate 1.96 per cent) the present worth is more than £3,000,000, while with an adjusted positive rate of 2 per cent the present worth is nearly £2,000,000. It is unlikely that the benefits would remain the same during periods of deflation and the figures given are deceitfully optimistic because the need for alterations to the basic data has been ignored.

Periods of continuing deflation are short-lived. Generally the aim of Government is to keep the cost of their borrowing in the region of 2 per cent or less, after allowing for the effects of inflation.

Taxation can also have an important bearing on profitability. Capital allowances reducing the initial capital costs and taxes on profit reducing the net return from an investment. Government grants may also be given to encourage capital expenditure.

CHAPTER 6

TENDERING PROCEDURE

Types of Tender

There are a number of procedures for establishing the price to be paid by the buyer to the seller. For goods ready for sale in the open market, the price first quoted will often be the price paid. Should the seller show a willingness to bargain, the price paid will still be that agreed at the time of sale. In either case, the buyer is likely to have an opportunity of comparing values and choosing from whom he will buy. When goods must be manufactured or supplied in accordance with the specification and instruction of the buyer, the seller may not wish to quote a price until after he has had an opportunity to consider the work and risk involved. The buyer may not be able to compare prices unless he calls for estimates from more than one seller.

The price for civil engineering works must, of necessity, be based on fairly detailed information supplied by the buyer, and he has a choice of three courses. A price can be negotiated with a single contractor. A limited number of firms selected by the promoter may be invited to tender. Tender advertisements can be published, offering an open invitation to all firms. Sometimes strong opinions are held on the relative merits of each of these procedures. It is suggested that it is unwise to hold predetermined views on such matters, as in each case the choice should be influenced by time, place and circumstance.

The Negotiated Tender

The negotiated tender has the disadvantage of not providing the promoter with comparative prices. Some think the price offered will usually be higher when contracts are negotiated. What would be regarded as a reasonable excess of negotiated prices over those obtained in competition is a matter of opinion. It has been held, on the other hand, that this excess would be diminished were it possible to compare the final sums paid. A promoter may prefer to run the risk of paying a hypothetical extra for the real advantages to be gained from the employment of a firm whose methods and policies are known, and who have in the past proved capable of satisfactorily fulfilling special requirements; a higher price may be offset by better quality and faster completion. What criteria should influence the engineer when he is called upon to advise on whether or not a price should be negotiated with a single contractor? Primarily the firm chosen should be one in which the promoter and his engineer have confidence, and which is of known integrity and reliability. The work to be carried out should also be within the scope and experience of the contractor's organization. The contractor who has successfully carried out dock and tidal work for a port authority may not be the firm best suited to construct an office block for them. In certain limited classes of work there may be only one contractor who is capable of undertaking the job, and negotiation with him will be the only reasonable method of obtaining the tender.

The adoption of a negotiated tender could influence the choice of the form and type of contract used. For works of magnitude a target contract may make it easier for both parties to reach agreement on price. When it is proposed to have consultation at the design stage, so that the most effective use can be made of plant, men and materials, the contract procedure should be such that the savings in construction costs are reflected in the price paid. The initial invitation to tender should include information on the proposed contract procedure, as well as a brief description of the scope of the works, and the approximate dates of commencement and completion. If bills of quantities or schedules are to be priced, this can be done by either the contractor or the engineer. The priced bills are handed on to the other party for comment and agreement. In many respects it is probably more satisfactory for the contractor to undertake the original pricing. For the cost of any section of the work will be in part dependent upon the plant and methods used in execution, and the contractor is better placed for making such decisions. The allocation of overheads and plant costs against particular items in the bills is also best decided by the contractor. The engineer or his quantity surveyor can price a set of the bills concurrently with the contractor, and compare these prices with those in an independently priced set submitted by the contractor.

The criticism of a contractor's prices may include the questioning of the allowances he has made in his price build-ups for labour and plant costs. As such allowances are to a certain extent based on opinion, and can never be wholly verifiable, they can only be contested with confidence when they are grossly inaccurate. Therefore, prices in dispute should be referred to current rates for similar work obtained in competitive tender, after allowance has been made for any abnormal factors peculiar to the contract, in each case the criterion being not the opinion of the contractor on the probable cost, but a reasonable current rate. After agreement has been reached between the engineer and contractor, a report and the agreed price should be sent to the promoter for his approval and assent.

Selective Tendering

Selective tendering is the most popular procedure; it is also the most straightforward. A limited number of firms is invited to tender, and usually, but not necessarily, the firm submitting the lowest price is awarded the contract. The firms selected may be nominated by either the consulting engineer or the promoter; and it is important that these firms should be acceptable to both. It is unfair, as well as pointless, to obtain a tender from a firm if the promoter or his engineer have serious doubts about the desirability of employing them. Special considerations arise when either government departments or local authorities use selective tendering. When public money is spent, it is important to ensure that no contractor is deprived of all opportunity to tender merely because of prejudice or corruption, or for any other unjust reason. Both government departments and local authorities overcome this objection to selective tendering by advertising that they are willing to accept requests from contractors to be placed on their lists, from which selection is made for given classes of work within different cost brackets. References and some evidence of ability to fulfil such contracts are required in support of the applications. For each tender a selection is made from the approved list, all firms being given at least an occasional opportunity to tender. Opinions differ on the number of firms to be invited to tender for any one contract. The following numbers were at one time recommended by a government department:

Contracts below £20,000 . . . .   4 firms
Contracts between £20,000 and £500,000 . . . .   6 firms
Contracts between £500,000 and £2,000,000 . . . .   8 firms
Contracts between £2,000,000 and £8,000,000 . . . .   10 firms
Contracts over £10,000,000 . . . .   12 firms

These numbers are, of course, offered only for general guidance,[1] and six genuine tenders will often be sufficient, although fewer will be required for small works.

A report[2] published by the United Kingdom government in 1964 suggests a *two-stage* procedure for tendering which combines some of the features of both selective and negotiated tenders. Outline drawings and specification notes are issued to the selected tenderers with a request that they provide particulars of their material prices, labour rates, and overhead charges, together with information about their plant capacity,

[1] See 1977 Tendering Code for alternative numbers.

[2] *The Placing and Management of Contracts for Building and Civil Engineering Work* (*The Banwell Report*), H.M.S.O. 1964.

management policy, and other relevant factors. These data are evaluated and used as a basis for the preliminary selection of a single contractor who participates in the second stage. During the development and detailing of the scheme, this contractor is expected to assist and advise the professional team on all matters affecting the execution of the work. Concurrently, bills of quantities are prepared, and at the end of the pre-contract period a formal contract price is submitted. The report recommends that the terms of the preliminary appointment include a provision for payment to be made to the chosen contractor for his preliminary work should his final price prove unacceptable. The two-stage system is at present experimental, and there are a number of similar procedures in use which seek to combine the benefits of competition with contractor co-operation from the sketch-design stage onwards.

For many years there has been an unwritten standard of practice for selective tendering which, without being uniform, was generally adhered to; it has now been codified by the Joint Consultative Committee of Architects, Surveyors and Builders,[1] and its general principles are equally applicable to building and civil engineering contracts of all types. It lays down that the selection of tenders should be made upon the advice of the consultant and with the approval of the promoter, so that the final choice will be that of the firm offering the lowest price. The code does not mention the possibility of contractors offering alternative tenders which vary the tender conditions given by the promoter. Contractors should usually be given the opportunity of making these alternative offers, especially where civil engineering works are concerned. A contractor might be willing to offer a lower price for either a shortened or extended contract time. He may also wish to carry out the work in a different sequence and by different methods from those shown in the tender documents. Tenderers should not be discouraged from putting forward alternatives, providing they also give a bona fide price for the tender scheme, and it is understood that the alternatives are for the promoter to accept or reject.

[1] *The Code of Procedure for Single Stage Selection Tendering*, 1977.

Although they make comparisons difficult, alternative tenders should be encouraged in case there is a real advantage to the promoter in the alternative designs, sequences, and methods of construction offered by the tenderer. These alternatives will be based on his practical experience in executing projects.

The list of tenderers agreed upon should contain a supplement of reserve firms who can be invited to tender should any of those on the main list decide not to accept the invitation. It should always be made absolutely clear that the refusal of an invitation to tender will not be held against the contractor, or prejudice his chances of receiving further invitations on future occasions. It is always possible that capital, plant and staff are fully committed on work already accepted by the contractor. Should further contracts be obtained, more capital and extra staff will be needed. Sometimes expansion on these lines is neither desirable nor possible. The contractor should always be encouraged to reject an invitation in these circumstances, because his alternative is to submit a price so high that it will ensure his tender is not acceptable.

The code requires the following information to be given in the letter of invitation: the name of the promoter and his engineer, and the names of his quantity surveyor and other consultants with supervisory duties; details of the form of contract to be used; a brief description of the works supplemented by an indication of the structural techniques sufficient to enable the tenderers to gauge the character and scope of the works; the proposed starting date of the work, and the time allowed for completion; the tentative date for the despatch of the tender documents, and the time allowed for preparing tenders; a reminder that the acceptance of the tender offer will bind the contractor not to disclose his tender to anybody before the time for the receipt of the tenders; the number of additional copies of the bills which the tenderer will require to purchase in addition to the two or more free copies it is proposed to send him; and the length of time that the invitation will be open for acceptance.

---

[1] See *Code for Model Form of Invitation.*

Diverse opinions are held about the time for completion being fixed by the promoter, as it can be argued that in most circumstances contractors are the best judges of what is a reasonable completion time. Moreover time and cost are interrelated. Both these objections to the completion date being stipulated in the tender documents are resolved if the contractor is informed that he may submit an alternative tender based on a contract time of his own choice. On the other hand, the criticism that a true comparison of tenders is not possible when the time for completion and the price are both the subject of competition seems unanswerable.

The code also suggests that a condition of tender should be that errors in arithmetic or palpable errors in pricing should be corrected in such a way as to leave the tender sum unaltered. The sending out of the invitations should not be left too late; about six to eight weeks before the despatch of the tender documents is recommended as a reasonable time. Shortly before the despatch of the tender document, the tentative dates should be confirmed. The tender documents should include two copies of the form of tender, one addressed envelope for the return of the form, endorsed with the name of the job and time of delivery expressed as a specified hour of the day, instructions for the return of the tender, a complete set of the contract drawings, the specification, and two copies of the bills of quantities or schedule of prices. The bills will not be supplied when lump sum contracts based on the tenderer's own quantities are called for. Neither will a complete set of drawings be issued when the building quantities contract is used, although it is recommended that the tenderers are sent a set of small scale general arrangement drawings when the J.C.T. quantities contract is used. These drawings will be solely for giving the contractor an idea of his plant planning, handling and lifting problems.

Where the contract price fluctuations clause is included as a special condition in the I.C.E. contract, the proportions for labour, plant and various materials to be used in calculating the price fluctuation factor shall be tabulated by the employer prior to inviting tenders. The price fluctuation factor is calculated from the sum of these proportions adjusted relative to the appropriate construction indices. The base index is that applicable to a date forty-two days prior to the date of return of tenders. With the J.C.T. contract the basic rates of labour will be those most recently announced, and they may not yet have come into force. The basic prices of materials in the J.C.T. contract should be the market prices prevailing at the date of the tender. A certain amount of confusion exists as to whether the prevailing prices are those actually ruling at the tender date, or would include future fluctuations that have been published, but have not yet taken effect. It is suggested that the tender documents, regardless of the form used, should explicitly state whether or not the actual price payable for both material and labour on the date of tender is acceptable as the basic price. When it is expressly stated that the basic prices are to include for fluctuations which have still to take effect, the date on which future known increases are to be determined should be fixed at least seven days before the date for submitting the tenders. This will enable the estimator to complete his work without the need for hurried adjustments to his figures at the last minute.[1]

Examination of Tenders

Tenders accompanied by priced bills of quantities can be delivered by hand or by post, but those delivered after the time stated on the tender envelope should not be considered, as tenderers often circulate their prices immediately after this time limit is reached. Tenders are sometimes opened by the consulting engineer without either the promoter or the tenderers being present. The promoter should always be invited to be present, and he may require the tenders to be delivered and opened at his own offices. Local authorities and government departments will usually stipulate this, and their procedure will be regulated by standing orders. Each tenderer should be notified of the results as soon as possible. The quickest and

[1] Formulae adjustment by indices prepared by a government agency are now in use. See p. 218.

most courteous method is to invite the tenderers to be present when the tenders are opened, and if this is not possible, they should be notified by post without delay. The notification of the results cannot be coincident with the acceptance of a tender. This must wait until the bills of quantities have been checked arithmetically and received a thorough technical scrutiny. It is as well to request the three lowest tenderers to keep their offers open until this has been done and the lowest tender found satisfactory. Tender bonds[1] which become forfeit if a tender is withdrawn are sometimes used, but there appears to be no good reason for their use. It is considered that the cost of preparing a tender is normally a sufficient deterrent to irresponsible tendering.

The methods used by tenderers to obtain their prices do not form part of the code of tendering, and they are not bound by any rules when working out the prices. It is usual, especially with civil engineering works, for an appraisal of the construction problems involved to be made and for a preliminary programme to be prepared, together with a tentative plan of operations to precede the actual pricing. Co-operation will be needed between the estimators responsible for the pricing and the management provisionally selected to carry out the work if the tender is successful, if this appraisal is to be realistic. The plan chosen should enable the work to be carried out profitably for a price that is competitive. The relative reliability of such a forecast will depend on the extent to which the historical records of site costs have been linked with estimating data. The ideal situation is when the feedback of cost data is rapid, comprehensive and condensed. But there is a sufficient number of significant factors which are incapable of precise evaluation, such as weather and availability of skilled workmen, to make it impossible to forecast costs with any real precision for all but the most routine works. A blend of intuition and experience must remain a necessary skill in the preparation of estimates for large scale works until such time as a major advance has been made in scientific cost control.

---

[1] Tender bonds are usually required by U.S. Government.

The technical examination of the priced bills by the engineer or his quantity surveyor must therefore, in the main, be a search for obvious errors. It must always be carried out carefully as inconsistent pricing or an unusual method of pricing may have important repercussions on the final price paid. This is especially so where schedule contracts are concerned. It has been known for a contractor to inflate the prices of those items for which he is paid early in the contract, and lower those which occur later, so that the value of the earlier interim certificates is increased and assists in the financing of the contract as a whole. Though this device is possibly legitimate, its consequence is to inflate the cost of the foundation work, the quantities for which can be predicted with the least accuracy. Therefore the promoter may be faced with a final expenditure much greater than he would reasonably expect from a consideration of the tender figure. Whether or not action is taken to adjust such prices will depend on the amount of increase above average in the prices, and the expectation of serious variation in the quantity of the work.

Unrealistic unit rates should always be questioned, whether they are low or high. Estimates of labour and plant costs by experienced estimators can vary considerably, but material costs should agree within narrow limits, except in the case of costly fabricated materials. Obviously a price of £40 per m^3 for concrete ($20N/mm^2$) in retaining walls would barely cover the cost of the materials and the mixing; and a price of £120 per m^3 assumes a prodigal expenditure in plant and labour in placing that could be justified only in the most exceptional circumstances. It would be the consultant's duty to query either price. A watch should also be kept for inconsistencies in the pricing which result in a cheaper item being priced at a higher rate than those which are expected to be more expensive. If 6 mm diameter rods in stirrups were priced per tonne at a lower rate than 25 mm diameter rods in walls it would be reasonable to call for an explanation. Sometimes identical items in different sections of the bills are priced at varying rates. This will often reflect the deliberate acknowledgement of the contrasting conditions under which different sections of the work are undertaken; but if the varying rates cannot be attributed to such factors, they should be investigated.

When the bill descriptions are qualified by long, complicated and unusual methods of workmanship described in the specification, the rates affected should be checked to see that allowance has been made for the additional costs involved. Among contractors there is little uniformity in the pricing of the preliminary bill, and when a contractor does not price a preliminary item, or prices it at much below its real value, it is probable that the cost has been allocated elsewhere. Nevertheless, there is no reason why the contractor should not be asked to confirm such assumptions and explain why other items are apparently priced at more than their true value, when the differences are conspicuous. If the bills of quantities have been priced independently as a cost check during the time allowed for preparation of the tenders, they will provide a useful check when making the technical check of the tender bills. The tabulation of tenderer's pricing for each item, entered on ruled sheets attached to each page of the bills, enables differences and errors to be seen at a glance, and is a useful check if time is available for carrying out the procedure.

Correction of Errors

Should the arithmetical and technical checks of the bills reveal errors in the contractor's tender, these should be corrected and an adjustment made to the new total on the summary of the bills so as to leave the tender figure unaltered at its original value. Before this can be done the contractor must be informed of these errors, and given the opportunity to decide whether to confirm his original offer, or withdraw his tender. This procedure will be equally applicable whether the unadjusted corrections result in an increase or decrease in the tender figure. Should the contractor decide to withdraw his tender, then the bills of the next lowest tenderer should be called for inspection, and providing they were correct, or he agreed to confirm his price after the discovery of errors, he would be awarded the contract. Sometimes it will necessary to inspect the bills and consider the tender of the third lowest firm.

Though it is widely agreed that this procedure is correct in principle, it is not universally accepted in practice. It is sometimes felt that the promoter will suffer unnecessarily when a tender many thousands of pounds below its nearest rival is withdrawn because the contractor is asked to bear the loss of one or two thousand pounds attributable to an apparently genuine error, or the contractor will be unjustly penalized if the tender is not withdrawn because he must absorb the cost of the error, despite the fact that the keenness of his tender has already reduced his margin of safety to the barest minimum. Obviously such situations present great difficulties, especially when the refusal of an opportunity to correct the tender price would result in the withdrawal of the tender and the abandonment of the scheme because the next highest price was greater than the promoter could afford. As a general policy it is in the group interest of both contractors and promoters for the tender price to be irrevocable, although in each case the final decision must rest with the promoter. The advice offered by the consultant must be determined by the relevant facts and his assessment of the conflicting merits of the alternative choices.

A promoter should always be advised to refuse to accept a tender when, either by reason of palpable errors, or because of consistently low rates, it is demonstrable that the carrying out of the contract at the offered price will involve the contractor in a real and serious loss. Experience will show that when contracts are undertaken at patently uneconomic prices, the outcome is generally highly unsatisfactory for both parties. It is true that in slack periods contractors may be willing to undertake work at cost for the sake of restricting their losses upon both plant and staff which would otherwise be unemployed, and there is no reason why the promoter should not accept such a tender. A distinction must be made between these tenders and those which are completely and disastrously uneconomic. The harm created by low tenders in times of depression is not a problem for the individual engineer, for the creation of an even flow of work under healthy economic conditions is a matter for planning in some shape or form by the state, though it may be found that such planning can never hope to be more than partially successful.

Should it be mutually agreed that a tender containing errors be accepted at the original offer price, the method of adjustment is a matter for negotiation, but it is suggested that the safest procedure is for all errors to be corrected so that a new total is obtained at the end of the summary page. This new total is then adjusted by the application of a percentage rebate or addition to the total value of the measured work. This percentage must never be applied to any p.c. or provisional sums in the original bills, and it is normal to exclude the value of the preliminaries from the operation of the percentage. An example of a summary showing both corrections and adjustments is given below:

Section

		£
1.	Preliminaries	200,000
2.	Earthworks	1,800,000
3.	Bridgeworks	800,000
4.	Concrete carriage construction	1,236,000
		4,036,000
Less **1 per cent rebate on value of measured work** (£3,600,000)		**36,000**
		4,000,000
Add 5 per cent for contingencies		200,000
		£4,200,000

The percentage is obtained by taking the total value of the measured work in section 2, 3 or 4 after the deduction of any p.c. sums or provisional sums in the section totals as shown below:

	£
Earthworks	1,800,000
Bridgeworks	800,000
Concrete Carriage	1,200,000
continued	£3,800,000

continued   £3,800,000
Less p.c. sums and their attendant percentages,
    and provisional sums   200,000
                      £3,600,000

The ratio is found by expressing the error, in this case
£36,000, as a percentage of the above value:

$$\frac{36,000}{3,600,000} \times 100 = 1 \text{ per cent}$$

The error in the example just given occurs within the
measured work. If the errors had been related to the preliminaries or the p.c. sums or in the extension of the percentage for
contingencies the correction would be made in the same
manner, but the percentage would nevertheless be expressed as
a ratio of the measured work. A further example illustrating
such a procedure is given below:

	£
Preliminaries	120,000
Earthworks	680,000
Reinforced concrete construction	1,200,000
	2,000,000

Add **2 per cent percentage addition on value of
measured work** (£1,500,000) **30,000**
                      2,030,000
Add 2½ per cent for contingencies (say)   50,000
                  £2,080,000

	£
Earthworks	680,000
Reinforced concrete	1,200,000
	1,880,000
Less p.c. sums and their attendant percentages	380,000
	£1,500,000

$$\text{Ratio} = \frac{30,000}{1,500,000} \times 100 = 2 \text{ per cent}$$

In practice the percentage may extend to four or more places of decimals. If this is so the percentage can be rounded off provided the resultant discrepancy does not exceed £10 or thereabouts, a small correction to the tender figure being preferable to a tedious and time wasting series of decimal places. The contract bills must be endorsed to the effect that this adjustment should be applied to the final value of the measured work, and to the value of the measured work included in interim valuations. The endorsement must be signed by both parties. This endorsement should be added to every copy of the priced bills. This method of correction will apply solely to errors in the contractor's pricing found before the contract is signed. Errors in the quantities found by either the tenderer or the consultant after the receipt of the tenders will be adjusted after the signing of the contract, and treated as variations.

If tenderers, when pricing the bills and preparing their tenders, should discover any ambiguities in the documents, or have any doubts on any matter, they should communicate their queries to the consulting engineer. Often queries raised by one tenderer will not be noticed by another, so it is important that the answers to the queries of one contractor are circulated in writing to all tenderers, whether they concern supplementary information or amendments to the descriptions of quantities in the contract documents. This should apply however trivial the subject of the queries may seem. Occasionally contractors will approach the engineer either with a suggestion for a change in the design, or to ask a question on temporary site works, upon which it is not the consulting engineer's duty to advise them. Where a change of design is concerned, the proper approach is for an alternative tender to be submitted, and the design of temporary site works will often be entirely within the contractor's jurisdiction. However, the consulting engineer should always study the point raised carefully, as sometimes it is difficult to distinguish between one type of query and another.

Errors in pricing which are not detected until after the contract is signed cannot be rectified, and the contractor must accept any loss or gain involved, although rectification may, in certain circumstances, be allowed.[1] Problems arise on the treatment of these undetected errors in the final account when the new quantities differ from those in the original bills. Assuming a contractor priced 1000 m^2 of concrete floor in one section of the bills at 87p per m^2, when elsewhere a price of £8.70 was given. Reason and equity suggest that if he is required to place 2000 m^2 of concrete floor, he should be paid for the additional 1000 m^2 at the corrected rate. The adjustment will be more complex when, as a result of variation, the whole of the 150 mm concrete floor is omitted and 2000 m^2 of 180 mm concrete floor priced correctly in this section is placed. Should the 180 mm floor which replaces the 150 mm floor be priced *pro rata* to the underpriced item omitted, and if the 150 mm floor had been originally overpriced would the same answer apply? It is suggested that when the whole of the work is remeasured, the fairest method is to apply the same principle recommended for the correction of errors found before the contract is signed, although this procedure cannot be mandatory for either party.

When errors were found in a contractor's tender and the promoter or his consultant failed to inform the contractor of these mistakes, the contractor had no redress. A case has been before the courts when a contractor claimed he was not properly notified of the errors in his tender, and alleged fraud on the part of both consultant and promoter. It was decided that there is no legal obligation for either the promoter or the consultant to inform the contractor of any errors in his pricing which they discover, but this judgement was coupled with the observation that if proof could be given that the concealment of the errors was intentional, it would probably be held that a charge of fraud would be justified.[2]

In the case mentioned it was proved that the contractor was directly informed of the errors on the telephone, and that the

---

[1] See Chapter 2.

[2] *Dutton* v. *Louth Corporation* (1955) 116 E.G. 128.

errors were reported in the local press. But the contractor did not receive a detailed report in writing. It must be emphasized that negotiations between the receipt of a tender and the signing of a contract must be properly recorded in letters; and any amendments or exclusion for the contract documents should be recorded in such a way that both parties have no excuse for denying afterwards knowledge of the exact terms of the final agreement.

Promoters have no grounds for complaints if, as a result of the publication of tender results, or the notification of errors, the lowest tenderer withdraws his offer, even though this means that the promoter must pay a significantly greater sum for the work he requires to be undertaken. A promoter withheld fees on these grounds, and when the architects sued for payment they won their case.[1] The judge in this case commented "that in the end one usually got more or less what one paid for".

A promoter may wish for one reason or another to avoid publicity for his undertaking, and not want the tender results to be printed in the public press. Contractors will usually refuse to accept tender conditions which prevent them from divulging their tender price once the tenders have been submitted but there would appear to be no objection to the inclusion in the tender invitation of a requirement that the tenderers should not reveal the tender sums to the press. Such provisions should only be made a condition of tender in special cases. Some promoters publish the value of contracts awarded; others publish unit rates. Unit rates are a useful indication of cost trends but should always be used with caution by the readers of technical journals as they are often affected by subsidiary factors and conditions which are not disclosed.

Open Tendering

When it is decided to allow an unlimited number of firms to tender there is a possibility that the firm submitting the lowest

[1] *Hasker and Hall* v. *Johnson* (1958). Unreported, but noted in *R.I.B.A. Journal* , October 1958.

tender may be unsuitable for carrying out the work, and a considerable wastage of time and effort is inevitable. Despite this, and the condemnation of open tendering in government reports and elsewhere, it is still not uncommon for local authorities to call for tenders by public advertisement. No doubt the reason for this deafness to exhortations to abandon open tendering is because it safeguards contractors from being deprived of tendering opportunities for unjust reasons, and protects local authorities from insinuations of favouritism however unfounded. A method of overcoming these difficulties by adopting open lists from which selections are made has already been described.

An illustration of the defects of open tendering occurred on one contract let by these means. The quantity surveyor reported that the bills of the lowest tenderer showed that many of the most important items had been priced at less than the cost of the materials to be used. It was therefore agreed to examine the bills of the next lowest tenderer. The quantity surveyor in his report on these stated that although no individual drastic errors could be pinpointed he considered the price was too low and the firm offering the tender too small to bear the probable loss. Nevertheless the tender was accepted. In fact the completion date was considerably delayed by the contractor. After completion, the contractor went into voluntary liquidation, and any small gain in price to the local authority was more than offset by the delay in obtaining use of the works.

Contractor's Alternative Proposals

Whichever system of tendering is adopted, it may sometimes be necessary to request tenderers to submit with their tenders outline information on their proposals for carrying out the work, with especial reference to the temporary works required. This, of course, will not be necessary where the works are of a routine nature, or the requirements of the engineer are fully detailed in the specification. Often civil engineering works present special difficulties to which either the consulting engineer cannot give precise answers in the drawings and the specification, or it is considered that it would be unwise to restrict the contractor to one prearranged method. When this is so, the engineer will often wish to scrutinize and check the contractor's proposals before giving them his approval. The study of these schemes before the tender is accepted should prevent misunderstanding at a later date. Also, the requirements set out in the tender documents may be differently interpreted by the competing contractors, and result in considerable variation in the prices offered. The cheapest solution may not be that preferred by the engineer. In connection with marine works, a temporary breakwater may be required. The choice may be between a pipe-line supplying compressed air, a floating structure, and a timber-piled breakwater, and the engineer may require modifications, or safeguards, before he agrees to the acceptance of one or other of these schemes.

Bulk Purchasing

Certain local authorities engaged in school building have formed a consortium for the purpose of bulk buying of fabricated building components with the object of reducing costs. It is too soon to give a definitive judgement on the success of such procedures, but there is no reason why such principles should not have an application to some types of civil engineering projects, especially when fabricated components are required where the major cost is in the preparation of the moulds and prototype.

See Chapter 3, page 70 for bulk purchases by the civil engineering promoter.

CHAPTER 7

INDEMNITIES AND INSURANCES

Indemnity Clauses

The responsibility for the cost of making good any damage to the works during the period of construction and the maintenance period will be defined in the contract conditions. Usually the contractor is required to accept liability and insures against this risk. Exceptionally, the employer either carries the risk or insures against it himself. The contractor will be responsible for carrying out the repairs or reinstatement without regard to the apportionment of insurance and indemnity liabilities, unless the contract explicitly relieves him from these obligations, or the destruction results in the frustration of the contract. The contractor will also be obliged to pay claims in respect of damage, loss, and injury to adjoining property which are either caused by, or are a consequence of, the works, and for which he has expressly taken responsibility. If persons are injured or killed, whether they are employees or third parties, the contractor must pay damages and meet other expenses to the extent of his common law and contractual liabilities. These liabilities are complex and there are significant differences between the indemnity obligations imposed in the various contracts. Indemnify means not only to protect against harm or loss and make financial compensation, but also to secure against legal responsibility. Indemnity clauses cannot prevent a third party from sueing an employer, but they do make it possible for the contractor to be joined in the proceedings and to be made to accept financial liability.

Linked with these indemnity clauses will be those requiring the contractor to insure against these liabilities. The insurance obligations are seldom identical to the indemnity requirements. The contract conditions, the terms of the insurance policies, and the statutory and common law obligations of the parties to the contract, together with those of sub-contractors, and direct contractors, taken in combination, create a maze of interrelated problems which defy simplification. Despite this, it should be within the engineer's capabilities to make certain that the employer and the contractor have between them insured against all insurable risks connected with the execution of the contract.

Types of Insurance Policies and Their Terms

Some general knowledge of the clauses and terms contained in insurance policies is a prerequisite for the comprehension and interpretation of the insurance conditions contained in constructional contracts, and the achievement of overall cover for both parties. There are two kinds of policies available for the insurance of property and machinery against fire, flood, storm or other damage. One is known as an indemnity policy. The payments made by the insurance company will be based on the damage incurred, less the depreciation in the value of the property. On new works depreciation will be either non-existent or negligible, apart from that on plant, but when existing works are insured only a proportion of the full cost of replacement can be claimed. The alternative policy has a reinstatement clause which commits the insurers to paying the full cost of replacement, no account being taken of depreciation, always providing the works are fully insured and that the reinstatement is of the same standard as the works destroyed. A pumping station of obsolete design with out-of-date equipment could only be reinstated so as to give an equivalent performance to the property destroyed. Any difference between the cost of this and a new pumping station of modern design and improved performance must be met by the policy-holder.

When properties are insured for less than their true value, the policy-holder will never be paid more than the sum insured. Sometimes group policies are held which give cover for many properties. When the property owners carry a part of the risk themselves, the insurance companies will only pay a proportion of any loss. This ratio will be equal to that between the sum insured and the true value of all the properties. This is known as an average clause and is usually expressly mentioned in the policy. The amount payable can be obtained by applying the following formula, with which is given an example in parentheses:

CLAIM SETTLEMENT (£200,000) =

$$\frac{\text{Sum insured} \ (£400,000)}{\text{Full value of property} \ (£480,000)} \times \text{Amount of loss} \ (£240,000)$$

The sum insured is always the maximum payable. If this should be more than the cost of reinstatement or, where indemnity clauses apply, the cost of reinstatement less depreciation, then the insurers will only pay the cost of restoring the property to its original standard.

Policies of all types invariably contain clauses which protect the insurers from the vexation of claims for trival sums. These are known as excess clauses and provide that there will be no liability to pay the first part of the value of each claim. This sum is known as the amount of the excess, and may vary considerably. Sometimes within one policy the amount of the excess is varied, the excess in respect of flood and subsidence being higher than that for fire. A contractor will usually find that the administrative expense of making claims for small sums above the excess outbalances the amount recouped. An alternative to the excess clause which avoids this disadvantage, while excluding the possibility of trivial claims, is the franchise clause which states that only claims in excess of the franchise sum will be considered. The amount of the franchise will vary and assuming this sum to be £1,000, then a loss of £999 would not be claimable, but one of £1,001 would be met in full.

Besides the cost of reinstatement, the insured may be put to further expense as a result of the incident. When existing works are damaged either alternative accommodation must be rented, or overtime may be necessary both to expedite the repairs, and to avoid dislocation of the business of the insured party. As there is bound to be consequential loss, to a less or greater extent, it is always advisable for policies to contain a consequential loss clause. For the insurers will not meet claims for overtime and special temporary works in the absence of a consequential loss clause.

The payment of professional fees in connection with the reinstatement will not be covered by the consequential loss clause; and the engineer should make certain that the amount insured includes the value of these fees. This is usually achieved by the addition of a percentage to the contract sum, or to the value of the existing properties. These fees must be only for professional services directly in connection with the reinstatement. The insurers will never agree to pay fees for the preparation of a claim, or negotiating with their assessors.

World-wide inflationary trends make it likely that in addition to the cost of reinstatement there will be additional charges for increases in wage rates and prices of materials. Policies should contain provisions for meeting these additional costs, even when the contract contains no fluctuation clause. It is of particular importance when the contract extends over a long period of time. Sometimes extensive damage to existing properties will enable local authorities to enforce compliance with new by-laws which increase the cost of reinstatement. These extras will only be met when explicitly provided for in the policy;[1] this should always be done because it has been known for new works to be affected by these provisions when damage has occurred.

Fire or flood may destroy documents, records, and currency belonging to the contractor, and tools, clothing and other possessions or his employees. The cost of their reinstatement will only be met when they are specifically mentioned in the policy. The value claimable on documents will be merely the cost of the materials, and a limit is imposed on the amount recoverable on currency destroyed. An employee's possessions will not be paid for when the employee has his own policy.

---

[1] Public Authorities Clause.

Excepted Risks

There are certain risks which normally are not insurable. These are referred to as the *excepted risks* in the I.C.E. contract. The excepted risks are riot, in so far as it is uninsurable, war, civil war or other hostilities and acts of corporate and organized violence. The I.C.E. contract also categorizes as excepted risks any damage resulting from the employer's use or occupation of the works for which a completion certificate has been issued, and damage due solely to the engineer's design. These two risks can, of course, be insured against, even though they are not included in the contractual insurance. Riot is an insurable risk in the United Kingdom at a reasonable premium, and also in other countries which have long records of civil peace. Riot may be insured against elsewhere, but premium rates vary. The prudent contractor will ascertain the premium rates charged before tendering for a foreign contract, because in some areas a high premium is payable for riot risk. He will also be wise to submit alternative tenders, one offering insurance against riot and the other excluding it. For his competitors may have assumed a riot was an *excepted risk* and the employer or his engineer may prefer to accept the risk involved rather than pay the high premium.

Obviously the contractor should not be required to pay for losses that result from errors in a consultant's design, but it should be noted that the clause in the I.C.E. contract provides that the exception relates to causes solely due to the engineer's design, and in practice it will often be found extremely difficult to isolate from each other the effect of poor design and indifferent execution when a failure occurs. It is good practice for the promoter of costly and hazardous schemes to insure against the design risk.

Insurance of the Works

It is usual for the sum insured to be the aggregate of the contract sum, professional fees, and the allowance for increased costs. Figures of over £200,000,000 are met with in hydro-power schemes, and tunnels and bridges may cost many millions of pounds to construct. In such cases it is the custom of the insurance companies to offer a *first loss* policy which limits the cover to at most a few million pounds. Whether such policies are accepted depends on the mutual agreement of employer and contractor; and the engineer will usually be asked to report on the relative merits of the *first loss* policy and complete insurance. It would be dangerous to suggest a general rule when such vast sums are at stake. Each contract should be considered in relation to its particular risks and the premiums quoted, although natural prudence may prompt the engineer to favour the complete insurance regardless of all other considerations.

Either premiums are increased or the sum insured is reduced after a claim has been made, unless the policy contains an automatic reinstatement clause which provides for the sum insured to be retained regardless of the number of claims made. As it is essential that the sum insured should not be reduced, all policies should contain this clause. Premiums, of course, may be raised after each claim.

Public Liability Policies

Insurance against the claims of third parties for personal injury or damage to their property is covered by public liability policies. But who are the third parties in relation to a construction site? Obviously, adjoining owners and occupiers of properties, passers-by and the public. In addition the contractor and his sub-contractors have obligations to each other at common law. If a sub-contractor negligently causes damage to the works, and the contractor recovers the cost of the damage from the insurers under the fire and special perils insurance of the works, the insurers may compel the contractor to claim against the sub-contractor and take the benefit of his claim. This factor may be of importance when the policy for the insurance of the works and the sub-contractor's third party policy are underwritten by different companies or syndicates; it is preferable to have all policies underwritten by one body in the case of large contracts.

Public liability policies will protect the insured against claims arising through the negligence or mistake of himself or his employees. They will invariably contain exclusions in respect of plant, transport, food-poisoning, and other matters which will normally be covered by special policies. There are occasions when a third party will be able to substantiate a claim in law even when negligence cannot be proved. It is important to have clauses in one or other of the insurance policies to guard against these claims. Often a major risk with constructional work is the danger of subsidence to adjoining properties. This risk will be excluded from a public liability policy unless a request is made for its inclusion. It is usual for subsidence arising from the contractor's negligence to be covered in the contractor's public liability policy, and subsidence arising from other causes to be covered by a separate policy protecting both the contractor and the employer.

Claims resulting from the acts of sub-contractors are excluded from the contractor's public liability policy and the sub-contracts must provide for adequate insurance against these risks. Premiums in respect of public liability insurance are usually based on the annual wages bill, which normally provides the insurers with a reliable index to the risks involved. Before the beginning of each year an estimate of the maximum wages bill is made, and the premium is calculated on this figure. A credit is allowed in the following year based on the actual wages paid. Generally the insurers will limit their liability in respect of any one accident. It is suggested that this limit on small contracts should never be less than £1,000,000, and that on large contracts the limit should not be less than £5,000,000. The degree of risk is not directly related to the contract sum which may be greater on a hazardous contract for £100,000 than on a straightforward contract for £6,000,000.

Employer's Liability Policies

The third type of policy required is employer's liability insurance. For though National Insurance provides for the compensation of employees for injury, the employer is still liable at common law to compensate the employee for injury due to negligence, whether his own or that of another employee. Premiums are based on annual wage bills, and the premium rate can either be an average for all trades, or different rates can be paid for each trade.

Only general principles have been discussed, and the engineer when called upon to advise upon or frame insurance conditions should always seek the guidance and opinion of an expert. Insurance brokers and solicitors who specialize in this type of insurance, and secretaries of some of the larger contracting firms, will often be able to clear up difficulties and point out pitfalls to the engineer.

Insurance and the I.C.E. Contract

When the I.C.E. form is used, the contractor is responsible, from the commencement to the completion of the works, to repair and make good at his own cost any damage to the works from any cause whatsoever apart from the *excepted risks* previously mentioned. He will also be responsible for any damage he may cause while carrying out repairs or remedial works during the maintenance period after completion. The causes of damage will include fire, storm, tempest, subsidence and every other possible cause apart from the *excepted risks*. The phrase *any cause whatsoever* in the context of the contract will be taken to have the widest possible meaning, and will include damage resulting from negligent acts by the employer. In conjunction with these liabilities there is an insurance clause which, while it does not reduce his indemnity obligations, stipulates that the contractor shall insure against all these risks. Both this insurance and the public liability and employer's liability policy must be taken out in the joint names of the employer and the contractor with an insurance company of whom the employer approves, and with terms that have his agreement. The employer must exercise his right of approval reasonably. He cannot disapprove of a company without giving reasonable grounds, or insist on the inclusion of unusual terms unless this was made clear in the tender documents. The policies and premium receipt must be produced for the employer's inspection when required.

The policy should include insurance against damage by fire, storm, tempest, flood, explosion and earthquake, together with any unusual risks that have relevance to the particular type of work or district in which the works are situated, such as underground fire in tunnelling works, or scour in marine works. All-risk-policies are available which are inclusive of every risk apart from the *excepted risks* and are the policies best suited to the I.C.E. contract.

Even an all-risks policy will not cover the cost of the repair and reconstruction of any work constructed with materials and workmanship not in accordance with the requirements of the contract. No insurance company will wish to give a contractor a guarantee against the consequence of slipshod work and inferior materials, although the bills of quantities can compel a special insurance item for just this. This exclusion of sub-standard work is limited to the cost of replacement of the defective work, and the insurers still accept liability for the consequent damage. Nor will an all-risks policy cover the cost of remedying the mechanical breakdown of plant or its wear and tear. The majority of policies exclude mechanical plant and it is normal for the contractor to take out separate policies in respect of plant and transport.

The policies must cover the full value of the permanent and temporary works, together with all plant and materials. The contractor will receive no more than the claim payments for reinstatement works. During the progress of construction the value of the property to be insured will vary from a small amount at the beginning to the whole contract sum at the end. It is possible for premiums to be arranged on a sliding scale so that they reflect the risk to the insurers, but this method is unwieldy and uncertain. It is far more usual for there to be a fixed premium throughout the contract, the rate taking account of the varying risks at different stages, and during the maintenance period. For the insurance must provide against the risk of damage or loss occurring during the period of maintenance, either as a consequence of the repair work, or from some cause occurring prior to the period of maintenance, but whose effects were delayed. It is quite possible that additional works will be carried out in conjunction with the maintenance work. The risks associated with these additional works must either be covered by the contractor's insurance or the employer's policy, which should come into force when he takes possession. Insurers will expect to be notified when additions or alterations are made to existing works, and will sometimes raise the premiums to cover the additional risks involved.

The contractor must indemnify the employer against claims for payment arising from damage to persons and property caused by the construction of the works, but Clause 22 of the I.C.E. contract excludes from these causes any breaches of covenants or easements arising from the construction works and any injury resulting *from any act or neglect or breach of statutory duties done or committed during the currency of the contract by the Engineer or the Employer his agents servants or other contractors (not being employed by the Contractor)* ... Owners of adjoining land can expect to enjoy the right of mutual support. Should subsidence occur as a consequence of the contractor's negligence presumably he must indemnify the employer, but this would definitely not be so when collapse is not so caused.

The I.C.E. contract obliges the employer to indemnify the contractor against all public liability claims covered by the exclusions to the public liability indemnity responsibilities of the contractor listed in Clause 22. Consequently when damage to persons and property occur, which give rise to third party claims, one of the parties to the contract will be liable to indemnify the other. But the only public liability insurance required by the I.C.E. contract is that covering the contractor's indemnity obligations. This would leave the employer without

insurance protection against those risks in respect of which he
has explicitly undertaken to indemnify the contractor if the
insurance is limited to that required by the contract. Usually
this would be unwise, and the employer has two alternatives
open to him. He may insure against these risks by taking out a
direct policy in his own name. Preferably, the bills of quantities
can include a provisional sum to allow for the cost of a joint
policy in the names of the employer and contractor against
these risks. The provisional sum should never be omitted and
the contractor be required to put a value on the cost of such a
policy at the tendering stage. For while he should normally have
no difficulty in assessing his own third party policy premium,
because it will be based on his own past record and the value of
the wages, it will not be possible to assess the premium liability
of the promoter without undertaking a detailed investigation
which is not practicable at the tendering stage. The bills of
quantities should clearly define the risks to be insured against in
respect of both public liability policies, because there are a
number of exclusions in the standard public liability policy.
Some of these are relatively unimportant, others will be
covered by other policies such as motor insurance, or will be
uninsurable as are war risks. Others will be essential to the
effectiveness of the policies, subsidence being probably the
most important. The two policies should be taken out with one
company and combined; they should give total cover against all
third party risks that are insurable. In fact, it is possible to
merge the two policies, a proportion of the premium being
payable against the provisional sum.

The appendix to the I.C.E. form provides for the limit of the
insurer's liability in respect of any one accident to be stated as
the minimum amount of third party insurance. It is better that
this sum is inserted by the engineer before the despatch of the
tender documents.

Clause 24 of the I.C.E. contract requires the contractor both
to indemnify the promoter, and insure against any claims
arising from accident or injury to any person employed by the
contractor, apart from injuries to them due to the negligence of
the promoter or his agents. The promoter's liability should be

covered by the public liability insurance for which a provisional sum is included in the bills. The contractor's liabilities to his employees at common law are complicated by third party relationships with sub-contractors. As has been mentioned before, it is preferable to have the third party policies of sub-contractors underwritten by the company or syndicate responsible for the contractor's policy, when practicable. It would be unrealistic to pretend that danger of personal injury could be completely eliminated from construction works. Nevertheless, it has been demonstrated that improved discipline in accident prevention techniques can reduce the number of casualties without increasing costs.

Insurance and the J.C.T. Contract

The insurance of the works is covered by three clauses in the J.C.T. contracts, two of which must always be deleted. The first, Clause 22 A, is identical in intent with the parallel I.C.E. clause, and requires the contractor to take out a policy in the joint names of the parties, but the *excepted risks* are not mentioned, and the phrase *from whatsoever cause arising* does not appear. In practice, the engineer or architect should make certain the policy has the same scope, and gives the same cover as would be required with the I.C.E. condition. It is made quite clear that the contractor can only recover the sum paid by the insurers. The next clause that may be used, Clause 22 B, puts the risk upon the employer, but does not require him to insure when the Local Authorities version is used. Should the risk borne by the employer be disproportionate to his financial resources, he should be persuaded by his professional advisers either to insure, or adopt Clause 22 A, while the contractor will do well to satisfy himself that the employer is capable of meeting the financial obligations if widespread damage occurs. Clause 22 C is for use with contracts for alterations to existing structures, and obliges the employer to insure adequately against the risk of damage to existing structures and the new works. The sum paid to the contractor when the employer carries the risk or insures against it will be calculated in accordance with the rules governing the valuation of variations, and need not be the same as the claim payment made by the insurers. It is expressly stated that in certain circumstances both parties have the right to determine the contract when existing structures are extensively damaged. With new works, should the damage cause the suspension of the job to overrun the named period of delay, an option is given to the contractor to determine. Whichever form of contract is used there will be an implicit right in some circumstances to determine. Flooding may not only damage the works, but it may make it impossible to construct them.

The J.C.T. contracts limit the contractor's indemnities for the works and other properties to damage resulting from his own or his sub-contractor's negligence. His indemnity obligations in respect of the works are contingent upon the inclusion of the clause requiring him to insure in the joint names of both parties. His indemnity obligations for personal injuries are only qualified to the extent of his not being liable for the employer's negligent acts, including acts of the employer's agents, and of the direct contractors he employs. Public liability and employer's liability insurance obligations are mentioned in rather general terms. Express mention is made of a provisional sum for additional public liability insurance, and the bills of quantities should provide that the combined insurance policies should give both parties the same overall and comprehensive cover that is recommended in connection with civil engineering contracts.

Insurance and the GC/Works/1 Contract

The government contract GC/Works/1 does not require the contractor to insure, and the authority accepts liability for paying the cost of making good damage to the work arising from any of the *accepted risks*. These are fire, storm, tempest, flood, earthquake, riot, civil commotion, civil war, rebellion, revolution, insurrection, military or usurped power, aircraft and King's enemy risks. Expressly excluded from the accepted risks is all damage to plant, temporary buildings and equipment owned or hired by the contractor. He is required to *take all reasonable precautions* to prevent or minimize loss and damage from any of the accepted risks. Also, he is obliged to make good the damage to the works from any cause whatsoever. The whole cost of this will be paid by the authority when it is entirely due to an accepted risk or the neglect or fault of a servant of the Crown, and where it is partly attributable to these cases they will pay a proportion. Payment in all causes will be assessed in accordance with the rules for valuing variations. The public and employer's liabilities are similar in intent to those of other contracts. Although the conditions of contract do not oblige the contractor to insure against these risks, or the risk to plant, and the residual risks in relation to the works, he would be imprudent not to do so. In comparison with other contracts the insurable risks are less extensive, but the provisions of the policies will be intricate.

Nuisance

Both the I.C.E. and GC/Works/1 contracts contain special clauses defining the contractor's obligations and duties with regard to road damage, and are of similar intent. Provided the contractor takes reasonable precautions to prevent damage to highways and bridges, the employer undertakes to indemnify him against claims for damages from heavy loads and extraordinary traffic. Where necessary, the engineer should incorporate items in the bills for the cost of strengthening of roads and bridges. The depositing on the public highway of spoil from the wheels or vehicles can be both a nuisance and a danger to other traffic, and may also constitute a criminal offence. This would usually be held to be within the contractor's power to prevent, and he must allow in his tender for the cost of cleaning the wheels of the muck lorries as they leave the site.

Almost insoluble difficulties are faced by a contractor who finds the employer or his engineer have, by the failure to provide drawings or other information, virtually repudiated the contract. Often the contractor may not be aware of the breaches until the end of the contract, and the courts may later decide that it is not permissable to allow repudiation entailing *quantum meruit* payments, for the reason that no such repudiation was made at the time the breach occurred. The Court of Appeal in British Columbia made such a ruling in connection with a hydro-electric project which included a dam across a river. During the contract a combination of natural events and design deficiencies caused the contractor much additional expense[1]. Usually the least uncertain procedure for contractors contending with such misfortunes is for them to claim the extra costs within the contract procedures as soon as it becomes evident that breaches have occurred. This calls for a continuous monitoring of the costs from start to finish of the contract.

Dirt, dust and disturbance are usually associated with construction work, and are an inevitable consequence of demolition operations. Objections can be raised by the owners and occupiers of neighbouring properties, who may seek injunctions and damages. Reasonable precautions on the contractor's part can reduce the grounds for objection; but drills and other tools powered by compressed air, and piling plant can often prove intractable sources of trouble. Both the employer and contractor will be subject to the provisions of legislation concerning nuisance and in particular to the sections of the Control of Pollution Act 1974 relating to construction sites, which gives local authorities powers for controlling noise. Where possible the employer should apply to the local authority for consents under the Act prior to inviting tenders and should incorporate their requirements in the tender documents. A British Standard Code of Practice has been prepared listing measures which can be adopted to control noise on construction and demolition sites.[2] In addition the employer and contractor will be under a common law obligation to prevent these

---

[1] *Building Technical File*, No. 6, July 1984, p. 59.

[2] B.S. 5228 [1975].

nuisances. On the other hand the adjoining owners and occupiers cannot bring the works to a halt, or in most circumstances, force it to be carried out in a manner so costly as to make it uneconomic. They may be able to restrain a contractor from using noisy machinery between 10 o'clock at night and 6 o'clock in the morning, on the assumption that it is reasonable to expect a night's rest, but would be less likely to obtain an injunction stopping the contractor using noisy plant between six and eight in the morning, because this could be classed merely as an inconvenience.

The I.C.E. and GC/Works/1 contracts put the contractor under an obligation expressly to indemnify the employer against claims in relation to nuisance; with other types of contract the employer will be protected to some extent by the public liability indemnity clauses and common law rights. Bridging and other river work may result in the pollution of streams and the contractor should always insure against such risks.

CHAPTER 8

FORFEITURE, DETERMINATION AND FRUSTRATION

Breach of Contract and Determination

Should a contractor fail to carry out the obligations he has undertaken, the employer may claim damages for breach of contract. In addition to the remedies given by the contract conditions, an employer may have other remedies at common law. Damages for breach of contract will not always be an adequate remedy. The appointment of another contractor may be the only sensible procedure when there is substantial default. The employer, however, cannot adopt this course unless the contractor has previously repudiated the contract and the repudiation has been accepted by the employer, or unless he acts under a *forfeiture clause* in the contract. The standard forms of contracts contains clauses that give the employer an express power to determine the contractor's employment and expel him from the site in certain specified circumstances. It is the employment of the contractor under the contract that is determined, not the contract itself; the contract remains in existence and both parties continue to have liabilities and obligations under it. These clauses are known as forfeiture clauses, although the term lacks precision. The contract obligations continue, despite the fact that the contractor has ceased to be employed. Bankruptcy or liquidation other than for the purposes of amalgamation and reconstruction is a further ground for determination, and probably the one most often invoked.

ACE-F*

Neither the I.C.E. nor GC/Works/1 contract contain clauses giving the contractor an express right to determine, should the employer repudiate his fundamental obligations, although the J.C.T. contracts contain just such a clause. But even with the I.C.E. contract, should the employer's default be so flagrant as to amount to a repudiation of the contract then despite the absence of an express clause, the contractor would be entitled to accept the repudiation and to treat the contract as being at an end.

Nevertheless, there is, of course, more room for argument about what is or is not a repudiation than about whether particular facts entitle the contractor to exercise his rights under a forfeiture clause. The courts construe forfeiture clauses strictly, and will expect the written notices and formalities required to be complied with to the letter.[1] There must always be an unequivocal act by the employer to show that he has exercised his powers under the clause. An express right is given to the contractor by the J.C.T. contracts to determine if the employer fails to honour certificates.

Any party intending to determine under a forfeiture clause must ensure that the conditions stated in the contract as giving rise to the right to determine have been satisfied, and that all correct notices have been given. It is essential that the party determining does not do so unreasonably or vexatiously. A wrongful forfeiture is likely to amount to a repudiation by the party wrongly forfeiting and this would give rise to a claim for damages by the wronged party.[2] Apart from these legal considerations, it should be borne in mind that the disadvantages and uncertainties that are met with when a contract is determined are usually such that it is inadvisable to resort to this remedy if there is any other practical way of overcoming the troubles that have arisen. Under the I.C.E. contract it is for the engineer to decide whether or not the contractor's breach confers upon the employer the power to determine, unless the

[1] *Drew* v. *Joselyne* (1887) 18 Q.B.D. 590.
[2] *Lodder* v. *Slowey* [1904] A.C. 442.

ground for the exercise of the power is the contractor's insolvency or assignment of the contract without the employer's consent. Under the I.C.E. contract it is clear that the decision whether or not to forfeit is to be the decision of the employer, but it is for the engineer to certify breaches which allow the employer to determine the contract. An engineer asked to advise an employer on this matter would be prudent to seek legal advice.

Bankruptcy and Liquidation

Bankruptcy, liquidation, or assignment without consent gives the employer using the I.C.E. contract the power to determine without the necessity of obtaining the engineer's certificate. The employer must notify the contractor, however, of his intention to determine, whatever the grounds may be. Under the J.C.T. contract the employment of the contractor is automatically determined without notice in the event of his insolvency, but he can be reinstated by agreement with the receiver to complete the works. Questions relating to bankruptcy or the liquidation of companies are likely to be less familiar to the engineer than questions relating directly to the contract works. An engineer approached for advice when such questions occur should consult a solicitor familiar with the operations of this branch of the law, or suggest that the employer does so. But it is as well that the engineer should have an outline knowledge of the problems involved.

One difficulty associated with insolvency is that the liquidator of a company, or the trustee in bankruptcy of an individual, has the power to disclaim certain classes of unprofitable contracts within twelve months of his appointment.[1] A disclaimer which is valid will put an end to the contract and place the employer in the same position as other creditors with regard to any losses suffered as a result of the disclaimer. The power of the liquidator to disclaim or adopt the contract does not override

[1] Companies Act, 1948; Bankruptcy Act, 1914

provisions in the contract which entitle the employer to terminate the employment of the contractor. The liquidator should always be notified of the determination, and, if he proposes to disclaim, the engineer should advise the employer to take legal advice as to whether or not it would be in order to contest the legality of the disclaimer. The employment of the contractor is not automatically determined upon the bankruptcy or insolvency of the contractor, but that event entitles the employer to elect to determine or not. The agreement of the liquidator must be sought before it is arranged for an insolvent contractor to complete the work. Discussion with the liquidator is advisable on this question, as his experience will usually enable him to give guidance on these matters. It is in the interest of both the employer and the other creditors that the contract should be carried out to its end as economically as possible. As a general rule, if the site organization of the insolvent contractor is inefficient, it would be foolish to allow him to attempt to complete the work, unless the contract is very close to completion. When the contract is in its early stages, there is little point in allowing even a contractor with an efficient site organization to complete the work, and it is extremely unlikely that a liquidator would permit it. Whether it is decided that the original contractor or a new firm complete the outstanding work, a final account must be prepared to show the value of the work completed by the insolvent contractor.

Grounds for Determination

Except in the case of the insolvency of the contractor the employer may only determine if the engineer has certified in writing that in his opinion the contractor has committed one or more of the acts and omissions listed in the I.C.E. contract. These are:

1. Abandonment of the contract.
2. Failure without reasonable excuse to commence the works, or suspension of the progress of the works for fourteen days after receiving from the engineer a written notice to proceed.

3. Failure to proceed with the works with due diligence, despite previous warning from the engineer.
4. Having received from the engineer a written notice to remove condemned materials from the site, or to pull down and replace work rejected by the engineer, failure to carry out the instruction after fourteen days.
5. Not executing the work in accordance with the contract, or persistently or flagrantly neglecting his contractual obligations.
6. Either to the detriment of good workmanship, or in defiance of the engineer's instructions, sub-letting any part of the contract.

There is no requirement of law that the engineer should hear representations by the contractor before issuing his certificate.[1]

If the engineer advises the employer to determine the contract he should be certain that the contractor cannot put the blame for his default wholly on the employer or his agents, and that alternative remedies sufficient to recompense the employer are not available. For instance, should delay occur, it should be of a character that liquidated damages would not compensate, if determination is contemplated. The criterion would probably be whether or not the failure to proceed with due diligence would result in the completion date being delayed an unreasonable time beyond the original contract date. The refusal of the employer to choose the less drastic remedy offered by the contract will not necessarily make the determination invalid, although it will probably bar the employer from claiming the additional expense of completion by another contractor. Neither will a slow-down in carrying out the works be a ground for determination when the causes of it are due to some act or omission of the employer or his agents. Conversely the contractor cannot plead that the employer's right to determine is nullified just because an act of the employer or his agents was a minor contributory cause to extensive delays otherwise not within his control. Should defective work be left unremedied, and the engineer's

---

[1] *Hounslow London Borough* v. *Twickenham Garden Developments Ltd.* [1971] Ch. 233.

instructions be flouted, the contract gives the employer power to employ another firm to make good the work condemned by the engineer. The cost of this work can be deducted from the sums due to the contractor. This milder alternative to determination may be chosen if it is practicable. Often it will be found too difficult to isolate the remedial work, or to obtain the recalcitrant contractor's co-operation to the introduction of another firm to the site. It is possible that the suggestion to introduce another firm will spur the contractor to fulfil the instructions that he has previously ignored. What the engineer must not do, after proposing to have the remedial work executed by someone else, is then to determine without warning. If it is decided not to proceed with the employment of another contractor to right the condemned work, then the contractor should be warned of this, and given further time to make amends. Once the engineer has given his certificate, seven days' notice in writing must be given by the employer to the contractor before he enters upon the site and expels him.

The engineer must be alert to the many possible problems arising from a determination (especially when it arises out of the liquidation of the contractor). Special consideration should be given to the provisions Clause 63 (2) of the I.C.E. contract which provides for an assignment to the employer of the benefits of any sub-contracts but which seems to be based on the assumption that once notice has been given to the contractor, the contract would be automatically determined after seven days. This is not the case. The employer need not determine immediately or at all. This means that a situation could arise where a notice given under Clause 63 (2) forces the contractor to assign even though he is still employed as the main contractor. Consideration should also be given to the difficulties arising out of sub-contractors materials on site[1] in circumstances where property has not passed to the employer, and to the problems of payments made to the contractor before his liquidation in respect of sub-contractor's work.[2]

[1] *Dawber Williamson Roofing Ltd.* v. *Humberside County Council* [1980] 14 B.L.R. 74

[2] *Re Tout & Finch* [1954] 1 W.L.R. 178; *Re Jartay Developments* (1982) 22 B.L.R. 134; and *Re Arthur Sanders* (1981) 17 B.L.R. 125.

Procedure after Determination

The procedure after determination, whatever its cause, is the same. The engineer's first duty is to ascertain the amount earned by the contractor before his expulsion from the site. The engineer may do this without reference to the contractor, or in conjunction with him. Obviously it is more satisfactory if the sum due can be established with the co-operation and agreement of the ousted contractor or, in cases of insolvency, with the liquidator. The sum due to the contractor will be the value of the completed work, together with that of the unfixed materials stored at the site. Constructional plant and temporary works including sheds and huts become under most contract conditions the property of the employer; and he may use both plant and temporary works to complete the contract, or sell them. The hire value of plant and temporary buildings and the proceeds obtained from their sale must be taken into account in the final reconciliation between the contractor and employer; but their value should be excluded from the statement showing the value of the completed work and materials stored on the site at the date of expulsion. An exact record should be made of the work completed, and a comprehensive inventory taken of the materials stored at the site, plant, temporary buildings, scaffolding and hoardings. The condition of the materials should be carefully noted and steps taken to protect them from deterioration and damage. Copies of the inventories should be taken for the use of the new contractor so that he can sign for their appropriation.

The employer is accountable to the dismissed contractor for the terms he agrees with a new firm to complete the work although the new rates of payment agreed must be accepted by the ousted contractor without question, unless serious negligence or fraud can be proved. It is prudent to obtain the approval of the liquidator to the new terms in cases of insolvency. The method used to select a new firm and establish the price to be paid should be that considered most suitable by the engineer. One procedure is to amend the original bills or schedules by deletion of the quantities for work already carried out. The adjusted bills need be only approximately accurate as the whole of the work will be remeasured on completion. Even so, the preparation of such bills will take time, and to minimize delay and reduce disruption, it will sometimes be advisable to prepare a schedule without quantities for the major items. Rates on this schedule would be agreed, and a more comprehensive document would be prepared after the new contractor had been appointed, and while he proceeded with the work. Another method would be to pay for the outstanding work on a cost basis and preferably a fixed fee would be negotiated. The assessment of the cost of completing work left half-finished will probably require valuing by daywork methods even when the remainder of the work is paid for by measurement. When time allows, competitive tenders should be obtained, but otherwise a single contractor should be speedily appointed.

Unlike the J.C.T. contracts, no provision is made in the I.C.E. contract for the insolvent or defaulting contractor to assign the benefit of any nominated sub-contract to the employer, and fresh agreements must be entered into between the new contractor and the nominated sub-contractors. Usually the nominated firms will be willing to enter into fresh agreements on the same terms as before, but if they refuse to do so, good reason should be shown for differences between the new and the old terms. All the standard forms of contract give the employer the power to make direct payments to nominated sub-contractors when an insolvent or defaulting contractor has failed to pass on sums previously certified to these firms. In most cases the employer is not compelled to do this, and the engineer must ensure that the employer will be in no worse financial position by direct payment than if he had left the nominated firm to obtain its money from the liquidator, although the legality of such payments in cases of insolvency was vindicated by the courts some years ago.[1] In the J.C.T. 1980 contract, however, the direct payment is mandatory where the nominated sub-contractor has entered into a J.C.T. nominated sub-contract (Cl. 21.8 – N.S.C. 14)

[1] *Re Tout & Finch* [1954] 1 W.L.R. 178.

Materials paid for by the employer and stored at the contractor's workshops or yards will be claimed by the liquidator as the property of all the creditors, unless it can be clearly established that property in the materials has passed to the employer.[1] Any urgent work required for safety or similar reasons should have been carried out by the insolvent or defaulting contractor before he leaves the site. When this has not been done, another firm should be called in to carry out these works as an interim measure.

While a final account will have been agreed for the partially completed work by the original contractor, he will not normally receive further payment until after the final settlement has been made with his successor, at the end of the maintenance period. Examples of the statements and summary that should be sent to the defaulting contractor or the liquidator are given below:

Contract for New Reservoir

Final statement showing work executed and materials delivered to site by Messrs. X & Co. Ltd. up to date of determination 12 January 1985.

	£
Value of work executed as attached account	12,000,000
Less direct payments to nominated sub-contractors	800,000
	11,200,000
Less previous payments on account	9,200,000
	£2,000,000

Statement showing amounts payable by Messrs. X & Co. Ltd. in respect of damages and other expenses consequent upon the determination of their employment on the 12 January 1985.

	£
Cost of completion by Messrs. A & Co. as final account attached	12,000,000
continued	£12,000,000

[1] See Chapter 10, page 190.

	continued	£12,000,000

Agreed value of completion under the terms
of the contract between Z Water Company
and Messrs. X & Co. Ltd. 11,000,000

		1,000,000

Liquidated damages 40 weeks at £16,000
per week 640,000

		1,640,000

Less cost of hire of plant, temporary   £
building and other equipment brought
to the site by Messrs. X & Co. Ltd.,
and included in Messrs. A & Co.
final account   100,000

Less monies received from sale of
plant and temporary buildings
sold by the Z Water Company 140,000

	240,000

Damages and expenses payable to
Z Water Company £1,400,000

*Summary showing the residual payment due to Messrs. X & Co.
Ltd. from the Z. Water Company on the completion of the
contract for the new reservoir.*

                                £

Balance due Messrs. X & Co. Ltd. for work
executed and material delivered 2,000,000
Less damages and expenses due to
Z Water Company 1,400,000

Amount to be certified to
Messrs. X & Co. Ltd. .... £ 600,000

Where damages exceed the balance due to the contractor, the amount to be certified will be that payable to the employer by the contractor. A liquidator would be required to pay the whole of this deficit, except when he had successfully disclaimed the contract. Whatever the reasons for determination, sureties should be kept fully informed, and efforts should be made to obtain their approval to each and every action taken to complete the contract.

A contractor under pressure from his creditors may sometimes approach an employer and request special payments in the hope that these will enable him to overcome his difficulties, and avoid liquidation. The engineer must investigate the circumstances carefully before giving the employer his opinion. If the contractor's embarrassment is only temporary, it will probably be advantageous to the employer to give financial assistance in the form of advanced payments, or by payments at more frequent intervals than is allowed for by the contract, so long as all the advances are properly secured and the employer safeguarded if this financial assistance does not succeed in its object. Such action on the employer's part, if successful, will save him from the disruption and inconvenience that is inevitable when the contractor becomes bankrupt, and possibly from financial loss as well. However, if the financial position of the contractor seeking assistance is already hopeless, then any aid given by the employer may only result in a worsening of the situation when bankruptcy finally occurs. The employer's accountants or bankers may be able to advise on this matter, but they will require to know from the engineer the amount of money already due to the contractor, and the extent of the work still to be executed.

The government contracts, provisions for determination[1] when the contractor defaults, or becomes insolvent, are similar to those in the I.C.E. contract. There are, however, further provisions giving the authority special powers of determination[2] for contracts of a duration that exceeds three months. No

---

[1] GC/Works/1, Cls. 45 and 46.

[2] GC/Works/1, Cl. 44.

reasons need be given as to why determination is enforced, and the contractor will be expected to carry out any further work including that necessary for the protection of what has already been completed. The contractor will be paid for the whole of the work he has carried out up to the time he leaves the site on the basis of remuneration prescribed by the contract documents; in addition he may claim any additional expenses reasonably incurred as a result of the determination. Should the contractor be of the opinion that he has suffered any hardship by reason of the operation of these special powers of determination he may refer the matter to the authority, who will make reasonable payment for such hardship as is proved. When special powers of determination are enforced, it is usually for the purpose of bringing a halt to the work for the time being, and the question of the appointment of another firm to complete the contract should not arise. An engineer concerned with the fulfilment of such a determination should remember that the authority has powers which would not be tolerated in a contract between private firms, and he must therefore make certain that the settlement is equitable and fair to the contractor from every viewpoint.

The nominated sub-contract can be determined for the same reasons as are applicable to the principal contract. But it will be the contractor who will be responsible for obtaining redress from the sub-contractor or the liquidator. Difficulties often arise after the determination of a nominated sub-contract, because it is sometimes impossible to obtain the services of another firm to carry out the work at similar prices, especially when proprietary systems are involved. The rights of the parties are not always clear when additional expenditure is incurred as a result of the determination. But it would seem that if the engineer steps in and nominates a new firm without reference to the contractor, then all additional costs will be claimable from the employer.

Should the contractor desire to determine his contract with the employer, either by reason of the rights conferred upon him by the contract in the case of the J.C.T. contract,[1] or because of

---

[1] J.C.T., 1980 Clause 28.

the employer's repudiation of the contract in the case of the I.C.E. contract, he must arrange for the preparation of an account showing the sums he is entitled to for the work completed and materials delivered at the date he leaves the site. Where possible, he should obtain the engineer's co-operation in the preparation of the account. The J.C.T. contract permits the contractor to remove all his plant, temporary buildings and unfixed materials from the site. When a common law right of determination is exercised in connection with the I.C.E. contract it is doubtful whether he could successfully lay claim to ownership of any plant, materials, or buildings on the site; when the determination is the outcome of the employer's insolvency, the liquidator would no doubt claim ownership of these things. The adoption of the contract by the liquidator will normally be in the contractor's interest, whether or not completion of the work is decided upon. Sometimes it is feasible for the contractor to convert the remuneration that is his due into a share of the capital ownership of the enterprise, and if the liquidator can give a guarantee that the works will be completed this procedure may offer the contractor the best hope of minimizing his losses.

Frustration

Sometimes a contract will become impossible to perform, although neither party is to blame. The event causing the impossibility may be a natural catastrophe such as a flood or earthquake, or the action of the state in introducing a law that makes the performance of the contract illegal. A contract is said to be frustrated when such events occur. "Frustration occurs whenever the law recognizes that without default of either party, a contractual obligation has become incapable of execution, because the circumstances in which performance is called for would render it a thing radically different from that which was undertaken by the contract . . . it was not this that I promised to do."[1] It must be emphasized that it is not hardship,

[1] *Davis Contractors Ltd.* v. *Fareham U.D.C.* [1956] A.C. 696, per Lord Radcliffe at p. 729.

inconvenience, or loss that decides whether an occurrence frustrates the contract, because these are accepted as contractual risks. Neither would the fact that some small part of a large contract was incapable of performance be a ground for invoking frustration. The Law Reform (Frustrated Contracts) Act, 1943, governs the effect on the parties of frustration of a contract, subject to the relevant provisions of the contract itself. The Act's major provisions are that money prepaid in expectation of performance should be returned, and that a party receiving benefit from partly executed work shall reimburse the other party a sum not exceeding the value of that benefit. Clause 64 of the I.C.E. contract stipulates that settlement in the event of frustration should be ascertained in the same manner as if the contract had been determined in accordance with the War Clause[1] which is dealt with separately as a special case of frustration. The principal rules for payment set out in Clause 65 are as follows:

(a) Preliminary items should be paid for in full or in part depending on whether they have been completely or partially performed.

(b) All materials, reasonably ordered for the works for which the contractor is legally liable to accept delivery, must be paid for by the employer whose property they become.

(c) Payments for any expenditure reasonably incurred by the contractor in expectation of completing the whole of the works.

(d) The cost of making good any war damage to the works ordered by the engineer.

(e) The value of any increases in official labour rates and material costs due to the event of war.

(f) The cost of removing plant from the site.

A contractor cannot claim that the contract is frustrated if he deliberately delays the progress of the work in the knowledge that a predictable event will enable him to avoid completion:[2]

---

[1] Clause 65, I.C.E. contract.

[2] *Mertens* v. *Home Freeholds Co.* [1921] 2 K.B. 526.

for instance if war seemed likely, or the delay in the completion of a sea wall made it possible that winter gales would make its performance impossible.

The I.C.E. contract is framed to allow the contractor to be compensated when events not contemplated by the parties occur. This, to an extent, will limit the effects of the doctrine of frustration when misfortunes occur. Clause 12, which provides for payments to the contractor when difficulties unforeseeable by an experienced contractor occur, should compensate the contractor to some extent for radically different conditions; but the employer cannot rely on this clause if the circumstances had so changed that what was expected from the contractor was fundamentally different from what was originally contemplated.

The J.C.T. contracts contain a clause setting out the procedure for determination should war occur, but they do not provide a procedure for other cases of frustration, nor does the government contract contain a frustration clause. In any of these contracts, should performance become impossible, the procedure laid down by the Law Reform (Frustrated Contracts) Act, 1943, would be applicable.

CHAPTER 9

LIQUIDATED DAMAGES, DELAY AND EXTENSION OF TIME

Delay

"Perhaps no extensive and multifarious performance was ever effected within terms originally fixed in the undertaker's mind. He that runs against time has an antagonist not subject to casualties," wrote Samuel Johnson. While experience will sometimes lead the engineer of today to take a less pessimistic view, all the standard forms of constructional contracts incorporate clauses which set out a procedure for dealing with delays.

Delay in the context of a building or civil engineering contract is not necessarily synonymous with "sloth" or "dilatoriness". It means failure to complete work by the stipulated time. Such failure *may* be brought about by sloth or dilatoriness.[1] It can also be brought about by the need to do remedial work prior to practical completion to remedy faulty construction.[2]

The contract document must either give a date for possession and a date for completion as is done in the J.C.T. forms, or give a time for completion expressed in weeks, as in the I.C.E. form. Sometimes the contractor is called upon to complete sections of the work in one contract by definite dates or within defined times for completion. When these dates or times are written into the contract (either the formal agreement itself or one of

---

[1] *Bramall & Ogden Ltd.* v. *Sheffield City Council* (1983) unreported.

[2] *Westminster City Council* v. *J. Jarvis & Sons Ltd.* [1970] 1 W.L.R. 637.

the contractual documents) they will be as binding as the final completion date or times for the whole of the work. In such a case great care must be taken over the expression of the method of calculating liquidated damages.[1] But this will not be the case when the sectional completion dates are shown only in a tentative programme or provisional progress chart. It is also possible that the contractor will not be given possession of the whole site at the commencement of the contract. Times may be quoted in the contract documents at which each portion of the site will become available to the contractor, or alternatively the completion of a prior section of a work may be the condition on which the next section is handed over to him. When this is so the documents should make it quite clear whether or not the intermediate completion dates are contractual.

When contracts are phased to allow for the completion of one section prior to the commencement of the next, it is important that when the employer requires an interlude between each section for re-organization, the length of time to elapse between the contractor finishing one section and starting the next should be stated in the contract. In addition to establishing the time allowed for the completion of the contract, it is also usual for the contract document to stipulate that no overtime, night, or Sunday work shall be carried out without the engineer's permission. This permission will not imply in itself an obligation for the employer to pay any of the additional costs involved. The I.C.E. contract excludes from this stipulation work that "is unavoidable or absolutely necessary for the saving of life or property or for the safety of Works" and "work which it is customary to carry out by rotary or double shifts". Sometimes the contractor may be faced with either having a gang stand idle for the last hour or so of the day, or engaging them in an operation which because it cannot be left uncompleted will involve several hours' overtime. It would be unreasonable to deny him permission to work this overtime. It is generally the expectation of the operatives that they will be given opportunities to work regular overtime, so that they can enhance their

---

[1] See later page 179–180.

pay. This is normally contrary to the official policy of the men's trade unions which, however, is not effective against the deep-rooted desire of the majority of the men to increase their current earnings whenever possible. As a consequence, it may be necessary for the contractor to offer informally a guaranteed number of hours' overtime weekly, if he is to obtain a labour force of sufficient size. In these circumstances it may be difficult for the engineer to refuse permission for these additional hours to be worked. Fundamentally, of course, the policy of restricting overtime is correct, and is in the ultimate interest of the contractor, because long hours inevitably reduce basic productivity.

Extension of Contract Time

Delay in the completion of a contract can result from a wide variety of causes. All the standard forms of contract make some provision for the extension of the contract time, thereby alleviating the contractor's liability to pay liquidated damages for delays not of his own making. Delays which can be entirely attributed to the contractor's method and manner of executing the works are invariably excluded from the causes that are recognized as entitling the contractor to apply for an extension. The I.C.E. contract permits the contractor to apply for an extension of time in respect of variations, increased quantities or any other cause of delay referred to in the conditions of contract, such as variations due to compliance with the Public Utilities Street Works Act 1950, exceptional adverse weather conditions, or other special circumstances referred to in the contract. The engineer must decide whether these special circumstances fairly entitles the contractor to an extension of time. The contractor's application should be made within a reasonable time, twenty-eight days or as soon thereafter as is practicable are the words used in the contract, and the application must give detailed particulars of the cause of delay. Even in the absence of a claim from the contractor the engineer should consider all the circumstances known to him at that particular time and make an assessment of the extension of time to which the contractor is entitled. This assessment shall be reviewed at the completion date and finally determined on issue of the certificate of completion. Therefore the engineer can limit his assessment at a particular time to the extent justified by the circumstances known to him at that time. The final extension of time can be granted retrospectively after the work is completed and the whole can be seen in perspective, provided the delays are not caused by an action of the employer. For it has been ruled that where delays are caused solely by the employer, the engineer has no power to allow retrospective extension.

The J.C.T. 1980 contract now imposes time limits within which the architect must grant or refuse the extension sought. When extensions of time have been granted during the contract, the standard forms allow them to be revised after completion. Although extensions may be granted retrospectively,[1] it is preferable for the engineer or architect to make a decision as soon as the effects of the cause of the delay are reasonably clear. The J.C.T. contract permits the architect to fix an earlier completion date having regard to the omission of any work since the architect allowed the original extension of time. This earlier completion date cannot be earlier than the original date of completion. Such reductions of the extension of time must be given at a date which will permit the contractor sufficient time to adapt his programme to the reduced quantity of work without disruption.

The contractor should never be kept in unnecessary suspense. The engineer should certainly not withhold his decision solely in the hope that uncertainty will goad the contractor into recovering the lost time. An atmosphere of anxiety is not favourable to efficiency, and it is suggested that a negative decision or reduction in the period of extension is preferable to the withholding of a decision when all the facts are known.

---

[1] But not if the delay was caused by the employer, *Dodd* v. *Churton* [1897] 2 Q.B. 562.

The interpretation of what is fair and the ascertainment of the extent to which delay has occurred are no easy task. Extra or additional works present fewer difficulties, as the evaluation of the dislocation and delay caused by them is mainly a technical matter, and the onus will be upon the contractor to give an estimate of the additional time required. The engineer will find it much harder to deal with claims for extension of time which result from special circumstances. The I.C.E. contract is intentionally vague about this, for the good reason that events which would lead to an extension on one job would not fairly entitle the contractor to an extension on another. It is suggested that the commonest events which qualify under this clause are as follows:

1. The adverse physical conditions mentioned in Clause 12.
2. Exceptionally inclement weather.
3. Fire, storm or flood damage.
4. Strikes.
5. Delay in the issue of instructions and drawings.
6. Scarcities of labour and materials which could not be reasonably foreseen.

This list is not intended to be exhaustive, neither does the occurrence of one of the above events mean that an extension of time should be granted automatically. The decision should hinge on the burden of risk which the contractor is expected to bear in this matter. As has been said in relation to risk generally, the contractor should not be expected to contend with uncertainties which are impossible to quantify in financial terms with approximate accuracy. Should the engineer decide to grant an extension of time, this will not entitle the contractor to recover any of the additional expense involved, unless he can claim that the expense is allowable by reason of clauses elsewhere in the contract. It does, however, relieve the contractor of liability to pay liquidated damages for the period of delay covered by the extension.

Clause 24.4 in the J.C.T. contract lists 12 "relevant events" which may give rise to an extension of time. These include *force majeure*, delay on the part of a nominated supplier or sub-contractor (which the contractor has taken all practicable steps to avoid or reduce);[1] and the contractors inability to obtain labour and materials in an unforeseen scarcity. This last "event" is particular to the J.C.T. form.

The inability of the contractor to obtain labour and materials in an unforeseeable scarcity this explicit clause is peculiar to the J.C.T. contract and if the relevant sub-clauses (24.4.10.1 & 2) are expunged from the contract then fluctuation payments will become allowable after the completion date unless the wording of Clause 38.4.8.1 and 39.5.8.1 are deleted as well. The omission of Clauses 24.4.10.1 and 2 would still allow the contractor to claim an extension of time for a restriction to the availability of labour, materials and fuels by the exercise of Government statutory powers (24.4.9.) The J.C.T. contract makes the failure to give the contractor possession on the agreed dates a ground for an extension of time, so that any restriction regarding the handing over of portions of the site, or stipulations as to method and times of access to the site must be clearly described in the contract documents.

Force majeure is a difficult expression. The term is used with reference to all circumstances independent of the will of man, and which it is not within his power to control; war, floods, epidemics and strikes have all been held to be cases of *force majeure*.[2] In the J.C.T. contract the expression is, in any case, largely redundant, as war is the subject of a separate clause, and most of the other coercive events are listed separately. The J.C.T. contract makes it quite clear that the contractor who has received an extension of time cannot give a nominated sub-contractor the benefit of this without permission from the architect or supervising officer. This is not specifically mentioned in the I.C.E. contract and would depend on the terms of the sub-contract.

When the I.C.E. contract is used the contractor can claim an extension of time in respect of the delays of nominated sub-contractors or suppliers only where they are for reasons

[1] *Westminster City Council* v. *J. Jarvis & Sons* [1970] 1 W.L.R. 637.

[2] *Lebeaupin* v. *Crispin* [1920] 2 K.B. 714, at p. 719.

which would entitle him to an extension. As has been mentioned before, it is essential for the contractor to have sub-contracts with his supplier and sub-contractors, which incorporate all the relevant obligations and conditions which are contained in his contract with the employer. It has been known for suppliers to go back on promises which were given to architects and engineers, but which the contractor failed to incorporate in the sub-contract.

Where a large number of sub-contractors are employed to carry out extensive works, the success of the main contract may well depend upon the skill displayed by the contractor in controlling and unifying the complex of independent works carried out by a large number of separate firms. Just as an engineer must allow for expansion and contraction in long lengths of homogeneous structures, so the contractor must devise his programme to allow for overlaps between the work of different sub-contractors, so that delay in progress by one firm and faster progress by another can be absorbed without upsetting the harmony of the job as a whole. The task of contriving a smooth programme out of a series of disjointed operations performed by separate firms may be made easier if the needs of each sub-contractor are studied sympathetically. The firm harried to start work prematurely with a consequent loss in productivity will usually be less co-operative than the firm which finds the contractor has endeavoured to reconcile his requirements with those of the overall programme.

It is not now possible in the case of either the I.C.E. or J.C.T. contract for the contractor to claim an extension for delays regardless of whether or not it affects the contract completion date. When a contractor plans to complete the works in twelve months, where the contract time is eighteen months, he is not entitled to claim an extension of time until the delay exceeds the six months margin he has incorporated in his programme; but in certain circumstances he may be able to claim loss and expense associated with these delays. But as time is intimately associated with cost, the proper and prudent procedure for the contractor is to request that the contract time be amended to coincide with his programme. If the employer would be embarrassed either by reason of a shortage of money or a shortage of time in which to prepare drawings, the retention of the original completion date should be insisted upon, and the contractor offered the option of withdrawing his tender.

Under the I.C.E. contract, when the contractor's rate of progress is too slow, and results from causes which given no grounds for an extension of time, the engineer has the right to inform the contractor in writing of his opinion. The contractor is then under an obligation to take steps to correct the situation. Should the contractor decide the remedy is to work night-shifts, he can make a request to do so. The refusal of permission to work at night in these circumstances entitles the contractor to an extension of time providing there are no alternative ways in which the lost time can be made good. Permission to work at night will not entitle the contractor to additional payment, and must not cause any unreasonable noise or disturbance. Should adjoining owners or occupiers make any claim for damages on account of noise or other factors connected with the night work, the contractor must accept the whole liability.

The terms and conditions of the J.C.T. contract in respect of completion and delays are more complex than those used in other contracts, and are listed below:

"Date for Completion" – is the original contract completion date inserted in the appendix.

"Practical Completion" is the date on which the architect issues a certificate of practical completion. This could be earlier or later than the "Completion Date".

The "Completion Date" is the revision to the Date for Completion taking account of extensions of time, and reductions of time for a shortened contract period resulting from omissions to the contract. The shortened contract period cannot be earlier than the original Date for Completion.

The J.C.T. contract states that the contractor must state the amount of delay for each event causing delay whether or not the delay is concurrent with other delays caused by other events. The effect of delay can be countered by the omission of work. This is allowable after an extension of time has been given. This earlier completion date cannot be before the original date for completion. Should this method of counteracting the delay be proposed it must be ensured that it is practicable for the contractor to be given sufficient time to adapt his programme to the reductions in work required from him; otherwise the possibility of a claim may arise providing the contractor has reasonable grounds for asking for extra costs.

Estimates of delay must be updated as may be reasonably necessary or as the architect may require. The architect has the option of revising the completion date during a twelve week-period following the date of practical completion.

This revision can extend the contract time or reduce it where a variation omitting work took effect after the last occasion the architect made an extension of time. In all circumstances the architect must give written notice confirming the previous completion date, fixing it later or making it earlier.

Liquidated Damages

All the standard forms provide for payment of agreed damages by the contractor when completion is not within the contract or extended contract time. These payments are known as liquidated damages. The appendix to the contract should record the amount to be paid for each day, week, or other period for which completion is delayed. This amount must be a genuine pre-estimate of the employer's damage, and the rate agreed should represent the likely financial loss or cost incurred by the employer if delay occurs. If the amount is not a genuine pre-estimate of damage it may be held by the courts to be a penalty. In such a case the employer can only recover his actual loss, not the amount of the penalty. The liquidated damages inserted in the appendix to a contract for the construction of a wharf should be related to the expected loss of profit of the wharfinger for each day that he is deprived of possession of his new wharf. It is intended to be a reasonable pre-estimate, and cannot be varied if for any reason the forecast is inaccurate. It is more difficult to assess the rate of liquidated damages for work which on completion will not be a source of direct gain to the promoter. The losses deriving from the failure to complete a trunk road are borne indirectly and are to some extent imponderable. The completion of the construction of a sea-wall delayed by two months may only result in the loss of amenity to the local inhabitants and visitors. In some of these cases it may be reasonable to base the damages on the equivalent loss of profit had the undertaking been a commercial development.

Although the estimate of liquidated damages is not expected to be precise, a court would refuse to enforce the clause if the damages were grossly in excess of a reasonable estimate. Damages of £1,000 per week, for instance, in respect of a small pump house which cost £50,000 to construct might be considered punitive.

Whether the parties use the term *liquidated damages* or the term *penalty* is not conclusive; the decision of the court will depend not on the words used, but on the practical effect of the clause. Substantial performance of the contract will normally release the contractor from his obligation to pay liquidated damages, even though the job is not complete in all respects. An employer could not claim liquidated damages in respect of a power station ready for occupation and operation just because an ancillary building not essential to its working was still incomplete. When occupation and use of an installation such as a theatre, or a railway track, depend on compliance with by-laws or the approval of a statutory inspector, the contractor will not be released from his obligation to pay liquidated damages until he has completed all the works in the contract which are necessary to the granting of permission for public use. When days are the unit on which the liquidated damages are based, it will be held to mean every consecutive day, including Sundays and Bank Holidays, unless working days are explicitly mentioned.

Clause 47 of the I.C.E. contract provides for liquidated damages to be paid in respect of delay in completion of any section of the works providing that the liquidated damages for each section are stated in the appendix to the contract. The J.C.T. contracts are worded so as to make liquidated damages for sectional completion unenforceable even though the amount to be paid in damages for delay to a section is stated in the appendix.

In a contract for local authority housing where the damages were stated as £20.00 per dwelling the court held that the damages were not payable because of the explicit wording of the contract conditions.[1] Should damages for late sectional completion be required when J.C.T. 80 contracts are used, the relevant clauses of the contract should be revised to make this condition explicit.

Sometimes an employer will seek part occupation or use of the structure before the official completion: this would normally deprive him of the right to enforce any claim for liquidated damages if the work is delayed as a consequence.

When no liquidated damages are agreed upon in the contract, the employer can still recover damages should the contractor fail to complete on time. Also when by reason of his actions the employer has lost all right to claim liquidated damages laid down by the contract he would still retain the right to claim damages if the works are not completed in a reasonable time. In both instances these damages are limited to the amount of loss which the employer can prove.

The engineer is required by the I.C.E. contract to certify the completion date but he is not required to issue a certificate of non-completion when the completion date is not achieved, while the J.C.T. contract requires the architect to issue a certificate stating that the contractor has failed to complete the works by the completion date when this is the case. The J.C.T. is not specific as to the time at which the certificate should be issued. Clause 24 however envisages the deduction of liquidated damages before the date of practical completion is finally agreed upon, and the possibility that circumstances could arise where a repayment of damages previously deducted would arise. Despite the issue of a certificate by the architect the demand for payment of liquidated damages is at the discretion of the employer, and it is advisable for the architect to inform the employer of any circumstances that might influence the

---

[1] *Bramall & Ogden Ltd.* v. *Sheffield City Council* (1983). Unreported but refered to in *Chartered Quantity Surveyor*, June 1984.

employer in the exercise of his discretion.

The standard forms of contract do not contain clauses entitling the contractor to additional payments if he succeeds in completing before the end of the contract time. These incentives to early completion are known as bonus payments. Occasionally they are inserted into the contract conditions. Among the reasons why they are so seldom met with are the difficulties associated with their application in practice. It is important to remember that factors valid in connection with an extension of time which will postpone the operation of a liquidated damage clause may not have the effect of allowing the contractor to extend the time in which to earn a bonus. Usually the work must be completed on time, or the delay be the entire responsibility of the employer if the bonus is to be earned. Neither engineers nor contractors should attempt to draft a bonus clause without the assistance of a solicitor.

Bonus payments can be arranged so that the contractor receives this extra payment provided he completes the contract by a target date. Alternatively, a daily bonus is paid for the number of calendar days between actual completion date and the contract completion date. Despite the difficulties of phrasing a satisfactory bonus clause, such clauses do provide an excellent incentive to the contractor. The loss of a bonus penalizes a contractor, and may often have a greater effect upon him than a liquidated damages clause. Variations and delays by the employer in giving the contractor information tend to cancel out the effects of bonus clauses. Engineers should always stress these points when a promoter is giving consideration to the inclusion of a bonus clause, and make clear to the promoter that his choice may be between variations and receiving the works at the required date.[1]

Time is of the Essence

The phrase *time is of the essence* means that performance of the contract within a fixed time is an essential condition of the

---

[1] *The Placing and Management of Contracts for Building and Civil Engineering Works (The Banwell Report)*, H.M.S.O. 1964.

contract. The effect of making time of the essence of the contract is that, on the expiry of the time fixed, the employer is enabled to treat the contract (if it has not yet been completed) as repudiated, and may dismiss the contractor. When the phrase *time is of the essence* is encountered in the conditions of an engineering contract, or in the preambles to the bills of quantities, it should be treated with some caution, and with due regard to the context in which it appears. For the courts are reluctant to decide that a building or engineering contract contains a clause making time of the essence, with all the drastic results which follow, unless it is clear beyond all reasonable doubt from the wording of the contract that the parties intended to bind themselves in this way. In contracts for the sale of goods or land making time of the essence presents less difficulty. If the goods are not delivered on the stipulated date, or within a reasonable time if no date is stated, the buyer can repudiate the contract. A wedding cake delivered a week after the marriage has lost its main value. A stationer's shop will not welcome a delivery of Christmas cards made on the 28th December. But the vendor retains what value is left in the rejected goods. Under a civil engineering contract the works must remain in the possession of the employer, as they are rooted in his ground. It is possible to repudiate a contract before the contract time has expired, but in practice it can be a very difficult decision to make. The use of the words *time is of the essence* more often than not makes complete sense in an engineering contract only when used in connection with works of a temporary nature which lose their utility after a given date, and when combined with the exclusion of an interim payment clause. A grandstand for a coronation and an observation platform for a solar eclipse are examples. The words might, however, be applied to a contract for permanent structures where occupation was crucial to the preservation of the employer's capital; cow-sheds for an expensive dairy herd which must have shelter from winter conditions in the fields are an example.

CHAPTER 10

MANAGEMENT AND SETTLEMENT OF MEASUREMENT CONTRACTS

Interim Payments

Contracts usually provide for interim payments to be made to the contractor at regular intervals. Payment is conditional on certification by the professional adviser, and the employer must honour the certificate by making a payment to the contractor before the time allowed for this expires. The sum to be certified will be ascertained by making a valuation of the work completed and the materials delivered to the site. A percentage of the value is retained by the employer both as a security against default, and to provide a fund for the cost of making good defects, if the contractor should fail to undertake these repairs. This retention percentage should not exceed 10 per cent, and often there is no good reason why it should be allowed to exceed 5 per cent. When a bond is provided, the percentage of retention may be minimal.

The I.C.E. contract provides for these payments to be made at monthly intervals providing their value is not below the minimum sum named in the appendix to the tender documents. This minimum sum should bear a reasonable relationship to the size of the contract, and 1½ per cent of the average annual contract expenditure would comply with this criterion. This minimum monthly payment should not exceed £50,000, however large the contract sum, nor be less than £1,000 when the contract sum is small. At the end of each month, the contractor must send the engineer a statement showing the estimated value of the permanent work completed at the end of that month, together with the value of any temporary works or constructional plant for which separate amounts are contained in the bills of quantities, and sums on account of materials delivered to the site. Before certification, the engineer must check the statement, and be satisfied as to its accuracy. Should it be at all necessary, he must reduce the value of the certificate when the contractor is unable to substantiate any of the amounts included in the statement.

On large and complex contracts co-operation between the representative of the engineer and contractor is recommended. The engineer will request his resident engineer to undertake this task, though he may well decide to delegate the detailed checking, measurement, and agreement of the valuation to a professional quantity surveyor. The resident engineer should always be available to advise the quantity surveyor, and give rulings on matters requiring a knowledge of engineering for their evaluation. Even when the resident engineer or quantity surveyor co-operates in the preparation of the valuation so as to minimize queries, it is important that the contractor submits a statement for which he takes full responsibility. A summarized statement will be sufficient when it is prepared in conjunction with the quantity surveyor or the engineer's representative. A statement prepared solely by the contractor should give sufficient detail to enable the engineer to scrutinize and check the make-up of the total claimed. The valuation should contain separate sums in respect of the following:

1. Preliminaries and temporary works.
2. Measured work carried out by the contractor and his sub-contractors (including materials supplied by nominated firms).
3. Payment for work by nominated sub-contractor.
4. Insurances.
5. Dayworks.
6. Adjustment for fluctuation (when allowed for in contract).
7. Unfixed materials.

The amount to be included in an interim valuation on account of the preliminary items can be ascertained by any one of the following four methods:

1. A percentage of the total value of the preliminaries is included proportional to the percentage of the value of the measured work completed by the contractor as shown below:
   - (a) Total value of measured work in contract bills £8,000,000
   - (b) Value of measured work completed at end of twelve weeks £800,000
   - (c) Therefore percentage of measured work completed ... ... 10 per cent
   - (d) Value of preliminaries in contract bills £1,600,000
   - (e) Therefore amount included in certificate for preliminaries £160,000

2. A similar percentage is included proportional to the aggregate value of the measured work and nominated work completed to date.

3. A percentage is taken proportional to the number of weeks the contract has been in progress in relation to the total number of weeks allowed for completion. Thus on a contract for which the time allowed is 100 weeks, and the preliminaries are priced at £400,000, after one week the contractor would be entitled to £16,000, and after twelve weeks to £192,000.

4. The value of each item in the preliminaries is assessed separately on the basis of expenditure incurred. This expenditure may be heavy during the early weeks of a contract, when huts, plant, and temporary roads must be installed before the permanent works can proceed at full pace. Assuming the value of the preliminaries to be that given in the examples above, the expenditure after twelve weeks on these and other preliminary items might well be in the region of £250,000.

Each of the first three methods has the advantage of simplicity, but the initial charges for plant, temporary buildings, roads and other temporary works included in the preliminaries bill, as can be seen from the above examples, are likely to be disproportionate to the values obtained by the application of a percentage formula. As the I.C.E. contract explicitly provides for the monthly payments to include amounts on account of any temporary works and constructional plant which the engineer considers fair and reasonable, it is demonstrable that the contractor will be entitled to the fourth method of payment. It will normally be found satisfactory in practice to assess separately the value of each item of plant and temporary works, and obtain the amount due on the remainder of the preliminary items by the use of one of the percentage methods.

When the bills of quantities prove to be an accurate estimation of the contract work, they may be used for computing the value of the measured work. If they are not, or schedules form the basis of the contract, then the monthly valuation must be based on the remeasurement. Whether or not accurate bills are available, the first operation is the compilation of a record of the work completed at the time of valuation. This is achieved by a tour of the site during which the extent of the completed work is either registered in note-books or recorded on diagrams or drawings. The major items should always be recorded on small scale sketch drawings. By the use of contrasting coloured pencils each month, for colouring or hatching the drawing to record the work completed, a record of progress is obtained that is visually more intelligible than the customary bar chart. Fair copies of these coloured drawings would not be made, but the original drawings should enable the engineer or contractor to perceive at first sight the general accuracy of the valuation after the completion of the calculations. The correctness of the record obtained from the tour of the site can be checked and confirmed by reference to the daily record charts, bonus measurements, material record sheets and labour returns. Following the site inspection, the value of the completed portions can be assessed either by pricing the approximate quantities of the completed work, or by establishing the percentage of the work completed in each section of the bill.

The duplication of effort which occurs when copious approximate measurements are required for each valuation should be avoided. This can be achieved when the remeasurement follows closely behind the execution of the work; and the dimensions are processed so as to enable them to be used for the valuations. Where this is not possible the approximate measurements for valuation should be systemized and prepared so that it is possible to use the same data in successive valuations without repetitive effort. These valuations for the monthly payments cannot be precise. Overvaluation and undervaluation are equally to be deplored, and either can seriously mislead both the contractor and the engineer. Attention to minute detail will usually be found to be self-defeating. The primary object should be to include an accurate cost for every major item of completed work, and obtain a reasonable value for the many minor items of small value. The engineer should be able to cross-check the valuation by comparing the sums expended with the forecast of completed work at the date of the valuation, shown on the contractor's progress chart. The contractor should make, each month, a detailed reconciliation between the sums included in the valuation and the cost incurred on the contract at the date of the valuation. This reconciliation will be both a check on the accuracy of the valuation, and a control for the contract expenditure. When significant discrepancies occur between the book cost of an operation and the valuation amount, the cause must be found. When the comparison shows a deficit the difference could be due to undervaluation, excess labour or material costs, or to expenditure on plant, unrealistic low rates in the original bills, or to alterations in the conditions under which the work was carried out. Similarly the opposite would be applicable when an excess is apparent. When an alteration in the site conditions makes the work more costly to execute, consideration should be given as to whether or not it is of a kind which will give the contractor a right to claim the additional expense from the employer. It is usually only possible to make a rough comparison at the time of the valuation, but it is important that an accurate reconciliation should be made not later than half-way through the following month. This will be dependent on the efficiency of the accounting system, which must be designed to produce the cost figure rapidly, and in the detail required for effective financial control. Then the causes of loss can be detected and rectified before they become irremediable. Sudden catastrophic losses due to the weather, site conditions, and plant breakdown can cause a deficit on any contract; but the slow steady accumulation of losses is more often than not the result of failing to maintain the financial control recommended above throughout the whole period of the contract.

The amounts expended on goods received from nominated suppliers should be included with the value of the measured work; and the claims for these payments should be supported by the invoices for these goods, and any amounts for packing, delivery or replacements not chargeable to the employer should be deducted. The invoice amounts should agree with the accepted quotations, and the supplier should be requested to justify any additions he has made to his price.

Each nominated sub-contractor requiring an interim payment must be told to submit a claim in writing. This should give separately the gross amounts claimed for completed work and materials delivered to the site, and show the total amount claimed previously. The application should give in addition some details of the composition of the gross amount. These applications should be examined carefully and any adjustments needed should be made. Sub-contractors' applications for payments are often hurriedly prepared, and, besides being subject to errors of judgement and arithmetical errors, are often based on a book cost which may not tally with the measured value. The courts have held that a main contractor, under the J.C.T. forms of contract, may deduct from payments certified as due to a nominated sub-contractor the "amount of any *bona fide* contra accounts or other claims" that he may have against that sub-contractor.[1]

---

[1] *Gilbert-Ash (Northern) Ltd.* v. *Modern Engineering (Bristol) Ltd.* [1974] A.C. 689.

Insurances will be added to the valuation by the addition of the appropriate percentage. Dayworks must be included in the valuation provided the items are approved and their make-up has been agreed with the engineer. The daywork accounts should have been priced, totalled and checked. When daywork overlaps with measured work, care must be taken to ensure that items have not been charged for twice. When the contract includes a fluctuation clause, the valuation should be adjusted to take account of movements in the cost of labour and the applicable material items. Although the presentation and checking of the claims may not be up-to-date at the time of the valuation, these should be presented monthly and not allowed to accumulate. On contracts where the fluctuations are considerable, approximate amounts may be included in the valuation for the period not covered by a claim.

The value of the unfixed materials can be found by making a brief priced inventory of the major items, and adding a round sum for sundry items. The I.C.E. contract states that the amount included for materials delivered to the site shall be such as the engineer may consider proper. The amount should not exceed the percentage of the value stated in the appendix to the form of tender. This percentage is generally stated at 90 per cent. The invoice value of all the unfixed materials on the site can be accepted, unless the engineer has evidence that the site has been used as a depot for the distribution of materials, or that deliveries to the site have been excessive. Sometimes contractors and sub-contractors will request payment on account for fabricated materials or machinery stored at their works.

Provision is made in both the I.C.E. and J.C.T. contracts for such payments to be made. Such goods and materials are to be listed in the appendix to the I.C.E. form of tender, and the provisions of I.C.E. Clause 54 apply, while with the J.C.T. contract Clause 30.3 is applied. Such offsite materials must be insured by the contractor at his own expense against fire, theft, and other risks. He will also be responsible for any loss or damage which occurs. The materials should also be kept in a separate compound at the contractor's works, and clearly labelled as the property of the employer. On receipt of payment, the contractor must send the engineer a certificate acknowledging that the goods have been appropriated by the employer. These steps are necessary to safeguard the employer's rights should the contractor become bankrupt.[1] Obviously if the bankruptcy of the contractor is a serious possibility, the engineer must either refuse to recommend payment, or arrange for the property in the materials to be transferred to the employer.

A typical example of a valuation for a contract lasting twenty-four months is given below.

CITY BY-PASS CONTRACT
Messrs. A. Engineer & Co.

1.8.85   Valuation for Certificate No. 6
Preliminaries

	£	£
Supervision, 6/24 × £144,000.......	36,000	
Temporary buildings, welfare, 6/24 × £72,000	18,000	
Office and attendance on engineer, 6/24 × £36,000	9,000	
Temporary traffic signs and signals, 50 per cent of £30,000	15,000	
Mixing plant 3 at £27,000	81,000	
Setting out ⅓ of £36,000	12,000	
Damage to roads	3,000	
Bond	30,000	
Temporary footpath 200 m at £90 per m	18,000	
Temporary road 100 m at £450 per m	45,000	
Temporary bridge	120,000	
Testing materials	6,000	393,000
Bill No. 2 – Site Clearance		
Bill total	75,000	
Add No. 25 – Felling trees not exceeding 610 mm girth at £60	1,500	76,500

---

[1] See Chapter 8, p. 163.

Bill No. 3 – Fencing	£	£
Chain link fencing 100 m at £60	6,000	
Close boarded fencing 50 m at £90	4,500	10,500

Bill No. 4 – Sewers and Drains

Bill total £150,000 – 40 per cent		60,000

Bill No. 5 – Earthworks

Excavate surface soil 1000 m at £7.50	7,500	
Excavate in cutting 4000 m^3 at £25.00	100,000	
Imported filling 6000 m^3 at £20.00	120,000	
Open drainage channel 300 m^3 at £20.00	6,000	
Trim and compact surfaces of embankment 2000 m^2 at £10.75	21,500	255,000

Bill No. 6 – Sub-Bases and Hard Shoulders

Bill total £132,000 – 25 per cent		33,000

Bill No. 7 – Concrete Carriageway

230 mm Concrete carriage slab 18,000 m^2 at £25.00	450,000	
Mesh reinforcement 20,000 m^2 at £7.00	140,000	
Expansion joints 4,000 at £3.50	14,000	604,000

Bill No. 8

Bill total £1,500,000 – 30 per cent		450,000

Bill No. 9 – Bridges

Bridge 1	£	
Cofferdams	60,000	
Piling	80,500	
Piers	90,000	
Prestressed beams	75,000	
Decking	19,000	324,500

	£	£	£

Bridge 2
| Cofferdams .... | 60,000 | | |
| Piling .... | 46,500 | 106,500 | 431,000 |

Bill No. 10 – Kerbing, Pavings etc.
400 m Pre-cast concrete kerb at £15 ..	6,000	
Pre-cast concrete paving,		
900 m² at £20	18,000	24,000
		2,337,000
Insurances, water etc. 10 per cent		233,700

P.C. Sums
Steel bridge fabrications	250,000	
Add for profits 2½ per cent	6,250	
Attendance	23,750	280,000
		£2,850,700
Less 3 per cent retention on £2,850,700		85,521
		2,765,179
Add materials on site 90 per cent		
of £62,246		56,021
		2,821,200
Less previous payments on account ..		1,950,200
Balance due	£	871,000

On receipt of such a statement, provided he is satisfied with its accuracy, the engineer should issue a certificate showing the total amount due to the contractor, the amount previously certified and the balance due. This certificate must be sent to the employer, and a copy of the certificate, or a letter reporting the issue of the certificate, should be sent to the contractor. Payment must be made to the contractor within the number of days stated in the appendix. Fourteen days is commonly allowed, and should the payment become overdue, the contractor will be entitled to interest payments. Under the I.C.E. contract this interest is payable at an annual rate equivalent to 2 per cent plus the minimum lending rate at which the Bank of England will lend to a discount house having access to the Discount Office of the Bank current on the date at which such payment becomes overdue, the interest being varied with changes in the minimum lending rate.

In 1981 publication of the minimum lending rate ceased and the I.C.E. conditions of contract standing joint committee now recommend that interest on overdue payments should be paid at rate per annum equivalent to 2 per cent above the average base lending rate of the big four banks.[1]

Usually, although differences of opinion about the amounts to be included in valuations occur, they are reconciled, but on rare occasions both engineer and contractor will each be convinced of the correctness of his own valuation, and the error of the other. These controversies can result from three causes. Disagreement may arise over the assessment of the quantity of the work completed, although this is hardly likely to occur when the contractor produces measurements in support of his figure, as the dispute is about a matter of fact which is capable of substantiation or disproof. Another cause of dispute arises when payment is withheld because the engineer is dissatisfied with the work carried out. More often than not the conflict will be about the inclusion of a payment on account of a claim which the engineer refuses to acknowledge as valid. Sometimes this difficulty can be circumvented by the contractor including a sum

---

[1] Amendment Sheet No.1 to I.C.E. Contract [revised 1979] Clause 60 (6) and I.C.E. conditions of contract standing joint committee (C.C.S.J.C.) Guidance Note (G.N.) 4 – Interest on overdue payments [April 1982].

in each valuation on account of the claim, and the engineer reducing the value of each certificate by this amount. Neither party concedes its point, and both tacitly agree to postpone further discussion until settlement is required at the end of the contract. This procedure will not be acceptable when the contractor urgently requires interim payment on account of these claims. Clause 60 of the I.C.E. contract states that the engineer has an overriding power to decide the amount to be certified. This power is qualified by the contractor's right to have any dispute or difference of any kind whatsoever referred to an arbitrator, and this reference need not await the completion of the contract in matters relating to the withholding of a certificate. The wording of this provision has caused considerable problems in its application. On a strict interpretation, it appears to allow an interim arbitration to proceed in the absence of the employers' consent only if the engineer has actually refused to issue any certificate at all in respect of a claim, and not in circumstances where he has merely undervalued the claim and issued a certificate which the contractor regards as undervalued. This problem has been dealt with in a reported case[1] where the fourth edition of the I.C.E. contract was used, and the quantities were prepared in accordance with the *Civil Engineering Standard Method of Measurement*. The contract concerned the construction of an underpass and a dual carriageway. The excavation of the trenches for the pedestrian sub-ways had been measured in cubic yards, and the bills of quantities also contained an item for the additional excavation and filling required for working space measured in square yards and priced at 120 shillings per square yard. The trenches for the main retaining walls had also been measured in cubic yards, but the bills contained no items for the additional excavation required for working space behind the main retaining walls. The contractors drew this fact to the attention of the engineer, and he agreed that "some additional item should be negotiated". Unfortunately, agreement could not be reached upon the valuation of this item, and the engineer let it be known that, if his proposals were unacceptable to the

---

[1] *Farr (A.E.) Ltd.* v. *Ministry of Transport* [1960] 1 W.L.R. 956.

contractor, the matter must be held over until the end of the contract, and submitted as a claim. The contractors were unwilling to accept this ultimatum, and requested that the dispute should be submitted to arbitration, and they informed the engineer in writing that their claim to date amounted to £85,080. Just over three months later the engineer wrote and confirmed his complete rejection of the claim, and in response the contractors notified the Ministry of their dissatisfaction with the engineer's decision and requested arbitration. The Ministry refused to arbitrate on the grounds that the work was not yet complete. Thereupon the contractors took proceedings against the Ministry so that it could be decided whether the dispute was one relating to the withholding of a certificate within the meaning of the arbitration clause[1] in the I.C.E. contract.

The judge held that this dispute was not about measurements, but about the refusal to include the value of certain claims in the interim certificates, and was thus a dispute about the withholding of a certificate. He ruled that though it was possible that an arbitrator might decide that the money had been rightly withheld, the matter should be referred to arbitration before the completion of the works, and without the consent of the Minister. Although it was not strictly necessary for the disposal of that case, the judge dealt with the possibility of a wider interpretation of the phrase "withholding of a certificate". He said –

"A *bona fide* difference of opinion between the engineer and the contractor about measurements . . . could not amount to the withholding of a certificate . . . if only as a matter of convenience one would not expect certificates given in good faith to be open to question . . . The alternative would open the door to constant reference to arbitration during the currency of the contract. Interim certificates of this kind are not final and conclusive determinations of rights as Clause 60(4) makes clear and for this reason also, one is not in my opinion likely to have been intended to be the subject matter of arbitration while the contract is running."

[1] Cl. 66, I.C.E. contract.

The judge does not appear, however, to have been referred to a decision of the House of Lords in 1933 which would be binding on him. In *Absalom v. G. W. (London) Garden Village Society*[1] an interim certificate was issued in the value of £10,842 but the contractor contended that the gross sum certified should have been £11,125. The House of Lords regarded the architect as having withheld a certificate to which the contractor was entitled. It is suggested that the correct interpretation is that an interim arbitration may be commenced if the engineer or architect has withheld a certificate *for a proper amount*, as well as if a certificate is completely withheld. This means that disputes as to valuation can go to arbitration during the contract as well as disputes arising because of the engineer's dissatisfaction with the work or his refusal to recognize a particular claim. At the same time the contractor must, in practice, show some reasonable grounds for contesting the engineer's ruling.

The clause[2] in the J.C.T. contract dealing with interim payments contains no explicit provisions for the value of plant and temporary works to be included in the valuations; but, in practice, it is usual to include sums for these items in the valuations if they are of consequence. Otherwise the J.C.T. contract does not differ significantly from the I.C.E. contract. Neither is the contractor entitled to interest on payments when interim certificates are not honoured; instead he has the option of determining the contract when the employer continues to default for more than seven days after receiving a notice from the contractor stating that he will determine the contract if he does not receive payment. Care must be taken to follow the notice procedure set out in the J.C.T. contract if this course is to be adopted by the contractor.

The J.C.T. contract provides for interim payments to be made at agreed progressive stages of completion of sections or parts of the works, as an alternative to the regular monthly valuation. This alternative is seldom adopted, and then only for contracts comprising units of repetitive work, such as houses

---

[1] [1933] A.C.C. 592.

[2] Cl. 30, J.C.T. contract.

and maisonettes. Such stage payments could be made on civil engineering contracts if the parties came to a mutual agreement on the matter, and it was feasible for stage payments to be calculated. For instance, on a pipe line of uniform dimensions and construction, the value of 100 m of pipe line could be agreed. Payment would not be made on completion of each 100 m, but at the end of each month the contractor would base his application upon the value of the total number of 100 m lengths completed. Uniformity is seldom met with on civil engineering construction; but should the possibility arise, this method can be recommended, as it eliminates the labour of preparing and checking the detailed valuation.

It has been advocated[1] that detailed valuations should be made at quarterly intervals, and that the intervening monthly payments should be based on an approximate assessment. It is also suggested that these approximate assessments should be based on sums computed from an analysis of the bill of quantities before the contract is signed, in a similar manner to stage payments. This method is well worth consideration on large contracts, providing there is likely to be little variation between the bill of quantities and the works as executed.

Advances on account are covered by Clause 40 of GC/Works/1, and its effect is very similar to Clause 30 of the J.C.T. contract. But where government contracts exceed £100,000, the contractor may apply, if he wishes, for a further interim advance at the end of the second week in each monthly period. These extra interim payments are intended to be only approximate, and serve solely as a device to reduce the amount of capital required for financing the contract. No period for honouring certificates is stated, and the contractor's remedy when payment is delayed or continually dilatory is limited to an action against the employer for damages when the delay, in all the circumstances of the case, is unreasonable. The amount of the damages reasonable in such an action is limited to the amount of damage actually suffered by the contractor by reason of the delay.

[1] *The Placing and Management of Contracts for Building and Civil Engineering Work (The Banwell Report)*, H.M.S.O. 1964.

Clause 66 in the I.C.E. contract stipulates arbitration procedures and states that reference to arbitration may be conducted in accordance with the Institution of Civil Engineers' Arbitration Procedure (1973). This procedure has now been replaced by I.C.E. Arbitration Procedure (1983) which defines the appointment and powers of the arbitrator, and alternative procedures to be decided at a preliminary meeting. These alternative procedures consist of either a hearing before the arbitrator followed by a published award which may include stated reasons; or a short procedure, where the arbitrator makes an award on the basis of the written evidence submitted and the answers to questions put to the parties by the arbitrator; or a special procedure for examining expert evidence.

Amendments to Clause 66 are currently (1984) being considered by the I.C.E. conditions of contract standing joint committee.

Retention and Certificates

The percentage deducted for retention in the example previously given of a valuation for an I.C.E. contract is 3 per cent. The retention for a contract not exceeding £50,000 is 5 per cent with a limit of £1,500. For contracts over £50,000 the percentage is 3 per cent. A bond gives an employer additional security. Consideration can be given to the reduction of the limit of retention to 2½ per cent or even 2 per cent of the contract sum when a bond is provided and the contract is a large one. Both the cost of a bond and the amount held in retention must increase the overall cost of a project, and the engineer should endeavour to keep these charges to the minimum compatible with the security required by the promoter. GC/Works/1 provides a retention of 3 per cent on works executed, and 3 per cent retention on materials.[1] The J.C.T. retention percentage is 5 per cent, but a lower percentage may be adopted.

[1] GC/Works/1, 2nd ed., Cl. 40 (2).

The percentage of retention taken on payments to each sub-contractor should normally be the same as the contract percentage. The limit of retention for each sub-contractor should be in the same ratio to the contract retention as the sub-contract sum is to the contract sum. Thus a sub-contract of £10,000 forming part of a contract for £300,000 with a limit of retention of £9,000 (3 per cent) should have a limit of retention of £300. The limit of retention for each sub-contract will always take effect when the whole of the sub-contract sum is included in a valuation regardless of whether or not the contract limit of retention has been reached. This procedure is explicitly provided for in the J.C.T. forms, but is only implicit in the I.C.E. and GC/Works/1 contracts. Difficulties may arise when very small sub-contracts form part of large contracts. For instance, the limit of retention on a £3,000,000 contract may be £90,000. The limit of retention for a sub-contract £500 in value would be only £15 if the same ratio was applied. It might well be considered insufficient, and it is suggested that when such difficulties are likely to occur it would be reasonable to amend the terms of the contract, so that the limit of retention for sub-contracts below a given amount was always calculated as 10 per cent of their value.

The I.C.E., J.C.T. and GC/Works/1 contracts all make provision for the release of half of the retention sum when the works have been substantially completed, but the I.C.E. contract limits the release to 1½ per cent of the amount due in respect of sectional completion. All three contracts require the engineer, supervising officer, or architect to issue a certificate of completion before the first part of the retention can be released. Before the engineer can issue this certificate, the I.C.E. contract requires the contractor to give a written undertaking that any outstanding works will be finished during the maintenance period. At the end of the period of maintenance, the contractor will be entitled to the release of the remainder of the retention providing the conditions prescribed in the applicable contract have been complied with. The I.C.E. contract requires that the second half of the retention money be released fourteen days after the expiration of the period of maintenance although the engineer can withhold on behalf of the employer a sum representing the cost of the repairs not yet carried out and work to be executed. The maintenance certificate need not yet have been issued. A certificate of completion of making good defects must be issued, and the defects liability period must have expired before the second moiety of retention can be released when the J.C.T. contract is used. The GC/Works/1 contract states that the release of the remainder of the retention must await the issue of the final certificate.

It is pointless to hold retention on sub-contracts which were completed during the early stages of the works, and where time has proved the sub-contractors' work to be satisfactory and shown that no further defects need remedying. The J.C.T. contract gives the certifier the opportunity to secure final payment to a nominated sub-contractor, if he considers such action fit, before the release of the second half of the retention to the contractor, and also provides for the limit of the retention fund to be reduced by that amount. The engineer has not this right when either the I.C.E. or GC/Works/1 are used. But contracts are drawn up to serve the purpose of the parties, so that the engineer, provided he can obtain the assent of both the contractor and employer, could release the retention held on a nominated sub-contract before the end of the maintenance period, if the circumstance warranted such a procedure. With all three contracts the parties' consent must be obtained before releasing the first half of the sub-contract retention prior to the date of completion. Both the J.C.T. and I.C.E. contracts require the certifier to issue a certificate of completion in respect of sections of the work completed and occupied by the employer before the end of the contract. The I.C.E. contract explicitly forbids the release of the second half of the retention until the completion of the last section of the contract, while the J.C.T. contract explicitly provides for the release of a proportion of both halves of the retention, respectively on the completion of a section and the expiration of its defects liability period. The engineer could adopt the J.C.T. procedure on an I.C.E. contract when he believed circumstances made it appropriate, and the consent of the employer gave approval to the waiving or alteration of the contract conditions.

Final settlement in the case of the I.C.E. contract must await the issue of the maintenance certificate, which the engineer should issue fourteen days after the expiry of the period of maintenance, if all the repairs have been completed, or as soon as the repairs are completed after that date. The J.C.T. contract calls for the issue of the final certificate as soon as is practicable, but before the expiry of the time named in the appendix (usually three months) following the latest of the following three events:

1. End of defects liability period.
2. Completion of making good defects.
3. Receipt of the necessary documents from the contractor.

Although the stipulation about the receipt of necessary documents from the contractor is absent from the I.C.E. contract, it is obvious that the engineer will not be able to authorize final payment until such documents have been handed to him, and he has had time to scrutinize them and complete his computations. It is the duty of the contractor to ensure that the engineer receives all the records and documents needed without delay.

The Final Account

It is the engineer's responsibility to prepare the final account.[1] The contract calls for complete remeasurement even when the bills of quantities are accurate. Sometimes the remeasurement may be considered superfluous, and in such cases there can be no objection to the engineer arranging for sections of the original bills to be accepted as the final quantities, subject to their adjustment for variations, as long as both parties to the contract find this procedure acceptable. More often than not it will be found wiser and more convenient

[1] Cl. 56, I.C.E. contract.

to comply with the contract conditions and remeasure completely. A final account should normally contain the following items:

1. Preliminaries as contained in the original bills with justifiable adjustments to items affected by changed circumstances and variations.
2. Remeasurement of the works. The billing of these in sections should always follow the pattern of the original bills.
3. Adjustment of p.c. sums.
4. Daywork accounts.
5. Adjustment of price of labour and material fluctuations clauses where applicable.
6. Recalculation of amount for insurances.

Often contractors claim an adjustment for preliminary items because an extension of time has been granted. Such claims are only admissible where the delay is attributable to an action of the employer, or has resulted from the effect of the adverse physical conditions and artificial obstructions mentioned in Clause 12 of the I.C.E. contract. When the claim is admissible, only reasonable additional costs which can be checked and agreed by the engineer should be put forward. The cost of supervision is frequently in direct proportion to contract time, and may be assessed on that basis. The cost of sheds, huts, offices, hoardings, and some items of plant can also be calculated on a proportionate basis provided allowance is made for the cost of erection, dismantling and transport, which should not be altered by the extension of time. The extra cost of temporary lighting will be affected by the period of the year in which the extension period runs. An extension during the summer period could mean that no extra cost was incurred, while a winter extension could justify a greater than average allowance. A recurrent problem with the adjustment of preliminary items arises from the fact that they are not always priced at what would be considered a realistic price. Sometimes they are overpriced, and at others underpriced. In these cases the principle to accept is that neither the contractor nor the employer must be penalized in relation to the additional expense, while there should be no adjustment on the original items for the contract work.

The contractor must be given the opportunity to be present at the time of measurement, and every effort should be made to arrange that the measuring takes place at times and on days convenient to the contractor, but if for some reason or another the contractor is unable to arrange for his surveyors to attend, the measuring must not be unduly delayed on that account. Often the choice of measuring either on site or from drawings will be available. As a general rule, it will be found that the measurements will be more accurate, and the time taken in measuring less, when drawings are used, although it will always be necessary to check the drawings on site to ensure that they tally with the work actually carried out, and that their dimensions are accurate. Discrepancies discovered between the drawings and the work as executed should be investigated. When the work has been altered because of last minute instructions by the resident engineer, or because of the exigencies of the site, the work should be measured as constructed. If the alteration is entirely due to the contractor's initiative, then the engineer must decide whether to measure the work as it was instructed to be performed, or as actually constructed. Assuming that a contractor reduced the bearing of a suspended slab from 100 mm to 50 mm, or increased the centres of expansion joints in a retaining wall, the engineer can, of course, order the contractor to undertake remedial work so that the construction complies with the drawing. But for one reason or another, it may be considered wiser to accept the contractor's work as it stands. Should he do so, it is recommended that the work should be measured as originally instructed, and the contractor informed that he must accept responsibility for any defects that result from his failure to comply with the engineer's instructions. Deviations from the engineer's drawings and the specifications are more likely to occur on small and medium sized contracts when the site supervision is undertaken by a visiting engineer. In one particular case the contractor was instructed to demolish and reconstruct a panel wall from which the concrete had spalled in depth; instead the wall was refaced with concrete, and a bonding agent was used to strengthen the adhesion between the new and existing concrete. The engineer responsible for this contract did not consider that an unconditional order to demolish and reconstruct the wall was justified. Therefore the contractor was paid for demolition and construction of a new wall, and told he had the option of either accepting responsibility for any defects that might develop in the repaired wall or reconstructing the wall. Where no risks of defects developing are possible, but the contractor provides an alternative of inferior quality, the engineer, if he accepts on the employer's behalf the inferior work, should pay only for the work as carried out so that the employer obtains the benefit of the saving. When embankments are seeded instead of being turfed, it would be inequitable to expect the employer to pay for turfing. The same reasoning applies when a rough finish is accepted, in lieu of fair face concrete, and the engineer does not insist that the work be remedied.

Record drawings must be prepared by the resident engineer to show the extent and depths of excavation, and the quantity of obstructions, and any other details which are not shown on the working drawings. The contractor must inform the engineer when work is ready for examination and measurement, and fair notice must be given before the work is covered up.

The presentation of the remeasurement bill may influence the order in which the dimensions are booked, and the methods used for processing the dimensions. The traditional method is to record the measurements in dimension books, transfer the measurement to abstract sheets, and prepare the bill from the abstract. The chief disadvantage of this system is that bills cannot be prepared until the measurements for a section are completed, and reliable valuations of extensive and costly sections will not be available until after the completion of the contract. Alternatively, bills can be produced for each sub-section of work, and these can be made available for the monthly valuations. Recently, attempts have been made to eliminate the operation of abstracting and billing. The dimensions are booked on sheets provided with rate and money columns, and carbon copies are made. The sheets can then be priced and extended, and the page or section totals incorporated in a typed account. Provided the operations are planned beforehand, there is no reason why a combination of all three methods, chosen to suit the needs of a particular contract, should not be utilized. The value of variations should be shown separately in the final account when feasible.

Variations must be ordered in writing by the engineer. This may take the form of a letter, written order, or drawing. It is always advisable to record the variation on a written order. When the engineer gives a verbal instruction and fails to make written confirmation, then the contractor must do so. Provided the engineer does not contradict this confirmation, it will be accepted as an authorization. The contractor will have no clear right to payment should he omit to utilize this procedure. It has been known for both engineer and contractor to be remiss in recording major variations in writing, and the recording of minor variations will sometimes be missed even on the best run contracts. A remedy is for those responsible for the remeasurement to keep a comprehensive list of all variations and alterations. Should this list reveal that variations have not been properly recorded, it is permissible for the engineer to issue the instruction retrospectively. Retrospective authorization should be avoided as neither the engineer nor contractor can keep a sound financial control where there is a failure to observe a strict routine for the record of variations. The engineer should issue numbered variation orders. The order should concisely describe the variation and, if possible, an approximate value should be put against each variation as it is issued. Besides sending a copy of the variation order to the contractor, copies should be sent to the resident engineer and quantity surveyors. The contractor should also have a routine for recording variation orders, and for noting the effects of variations on his progress and programme. The provisions for ordering variations are given in Clause 4 of the J.C.T. contract and set a seven-day time limit on the contractor's confirmation of an oral instruction, and a further seven days after the receipt of the confirmation is allowed for the architect to dissent where differences arise as to the definition of the work as a variation or for other reasons. Sometimes eager agents fail to note that instruction covers work already described in the bills of quantities, and occasionally consultants are not aware that they are demanding more than is required by the contract documents.

Under the I.C.E. contract the engineer can order variations if they are necessary for the completion of the works or which are for any other reason in his opinion desirable. The variations permitted include the following:

(a) Additions or omissions.
(b) Substitutions and alterations.
(c) Changes in quality, form, character, kind, position dimension level and line.
(d) Changes in dimension, specified sequence, method or timing of construction.

The engineer has also the power to postpone the work,[1] but the contract gives him no authority to expedite the work or incur extra costs in achieving a completion date on time when delays have occurred. Apart from the provisions of Clause 46 which allow him to notify the contractor when in his opinion progress is too slow to ensure completion on time, and is not for any reason which would allow the granting of an extension of time, and requires the contractor to respond by taking approved steps to expedite progress so that the work is completed in the prescribed time.[2]

The I.C.E. contract states that "no variation shall in any way vitiate or invalidate the Contract."[3] Consequently, if there are substantial variations, the contractor cannot rescind the contract. Obviously, there are limits to the effect of this clause. A variation which resulted in the contract for a small jetty for

---

[1] Cl. 40, I.C.E. contract.

[2] See page 177 for further comment.

[3] Cl. 51, I.C.E. contract.

motor launches being altered to include the construction of a quay for ocean-going vessels of heavy tonnage would not constitute extra work within the terms of the contract. Either a new contract would be entered into for the construction of the quay, or the employer would be held liable to pay the contractor reasonable remuneration for the work. The addition of a further half-mile of roadway to a contract for a trunk road twenty miles long would be acceptable as a variation. Sometimes it will be difficult to decide whether or not additional work can be classed as a variation, for the definition of work outside the contract is to some extent a matter of opinion.

Omissions and additions will sometimes significantly change the conditions under which sections or items of the work are carried out. For instance, a road and bridges contract included fourteen bridges to be constructed principally of standard pre-cast pre-stressed concrete units; twelve of these bridges were omitted, and were replaced by welded steel bridges. The contractor claimed that the moulds for the units for one bridge were to be used for all the other bridges, and that as a result of the variations, the cost of manufacturing was considerably greater. Conversely, if the number of pre-cast pre-stressed concrete units required had been doubled, then the engineer should be able to negotiate a reduction in the rates for the units. The reaction of quantity on price will only be important when the difference between the original and actual quantities are sufficiently big; above certain levels quantity will have little or no effect on price. It is not only wide variations in quantities that affect the price of bill items. The decision to deepen a basement may not only increase the quantities of excavation and new construction, but may result in a radical revision in the method of procedure, which may alter the actual unit construction cost. Concrete may be more or less costly to place because of the alteration in the amount of reinforcement used. Although every variation may affect the original rates one way or another because of these factors, it is obviously impractical and against the intent of the contract to review the rates in every case, and such adjustments are normally confined to those variations where the difference in cost is significant.

The contractor will not be entitled to additional payment when upon his own initiative he uses more expensive materials or adopts a more costly system of construction. Neither will permission given by the engineer to the contractor to do this constitute a variation except in special cases. Whether, or not, the extra costs are chargeable to the contract will depend on the reasons that prompted the contractor to seek permission to vary. The problem is illustrated by a lawsuit[1] of the last century when it was alleged by the contractors that it was impossible to cast certain iron trough girders to the specified weights, and the engineer orally allowed them to increase the thickness of the members of the girders. The contract provided that the contractors should not be entitled to make any alteration in the specified works without a written order of the engineer. On completion of the contract the contractors claimed a considerable sum for this work. It was held that there was nothing to imply the authorization of an additional payment. The contract documents in this case differed in many respects from those that would be used with the current I.C.E. contract, and it is possible that if a similar case arose in connection with an I.C.E. contract, the additional payment would be held to be allowable.

Sometimes the contractor will seek permission to vary the contract method of work for one of the following reasons:

1. It is more expensive.
2. It is more likely to develop defects.
3. It does not suit his planning programme or plant lay-out.
4. It is impracticable.
5. It is necessary to comply with injunctions or threats of injunctions by adjoining owners.

These reasons do not entitle a contractor to extra payment, except where it is agreed that the contract method is impracticable, but the engineer may issue a variation order authorizing extra payment in the other cases if he considers this justifiable. Obviously, when the permission is sought so as to comply with a statute or to rectify an error in the quantities or specification, the contractor will be automatically entitled to a

---

[1] *Tharsis Sulphur & Copper Co.* v. *McElroy & Sons* (1878) 3 App. Cas. 1040.

variation authorizing payment. As the causes for these variations are not always clear, to avoid misunderstanding, the engineer should always qualify his permission with a definite ruling as to whether or not the employer is liable for any extra cost incurred.

Where the work is based on a contractor's design, the wording of the engineer's permission is of particular importance. This is illustrated by a dispute in connection with a piling contract.[1] Although a revised edition of the R.I.B.A. 1939 contract was used, the ruling of the court has equal relevance in general to I.C.E. contracts. The contractors undertook to design and carry out pile driving work for the foundations of a block of flats. Site conditions were encountered which rendered it impracticable to carry out the work in the way it had been contracted for. In consequence, the contractors suggested two alternative methods of piling and suggested fresh prices. On receiving these, the architects wrote in reply "we accept your proposals that the piles should be of the bored type in accordance with the quotations submitted by your sub-contractors." Because of this letter it was held that "although the contractors could have had no defence to an action for breach of contract when it became clear that their design was impracticable, the architects' letter was an instruction involving a variation in the design or quality of the work within Clause 1 of the contract" (presumably Clause 51 would have applied had the I.C.E. contract been used) "and the contractors were entitled to be paid on the sub-contractors' quotation and not at the original tender price." It may be thought by some that in cases where adverse physical conditions were the cause of the variation, the revised price would be allowable under the terms of Clause 12 of the I.C.E. contract which enables the contractor to recover extra cost due to the conditions. Such additional costs are, however, only recoverable if caused by physical conditions which could not reasonably have been foreseen by an experienced contractor. Furthermore the contractor must follow carefully the procedures of Clause 12 if he wishes to make a claim.

[1] *Simplex Concrete Piles Ltd.* v. *St. Pancras M.B.C.* (1958) 14 B.L.R. 84.

Nominated Sub-contractors

The work of nominated sub-contractors should be remeasured on completion. The representative of the sub-contractor should have the opportunity of being present when the measurements are taken; and measurement and any new rates should be agreed before the account of the sub-contractor is rendered to the contractor. The amount included in the final account should be the net amount approved by the engineer, with an addition of 1/39th to cover the 2½ per cent cash discount that the contractor is entitled to when payments are made to sub-contractors by direction of the engineer before he has received payment from the employer. Profit should be allowed *pro rata* to the amounts in the bills upon the amount included in the final account, including dayworks and fluctuations. The contractor should let the engineer have copies of all invoices, accounts and credit notes. These must be tabulated and checked, and deductions made from the total claimed by the sub-contractor for items not chargeable to the employer, before a final figure is agreed with the sub-contractor. These deductions could include charges for breakages and work executed by the sub-contractor for the contractor, although agreement on the liability for payment of these sums is a matter for settlement between contractor and sub-contractor. The written confirmation of the sub-contractor should be obtained prior to including the agreed sums in the final account. Should an irreconcilable dispute occur between the nominated sub-contractor and the engineer, and the sub-contractor require that the matter be referred to arbitration, it must be done through the agency of the contractor. The engineer can demand reasonable proof that payments included in previous certificates have been made to sub-contractors. Local authorities and government departments usually demand that the receipts of payments to nominated sub-contractors are inspected by the engineer so that he can vouch that the contractor has settled their accounts before final payment is made.

The sum for attendance in the original bills should only be adjusted when the quantity, quality, or scope of the sub-contractor's work is changed. Variations in the value of the p.c. account for other reasons do not provide grounds for either an increase or decrease, even when the attendances are calculated as a percentage of the p.c. sums in the bills. An increase or decrease in the cost of piling would not justify an alteration to the sum for attendance unless the number of piles or their lengths are altered, or the method of piling was changed so as to vary the attendance required. Special items of attendance the contractor was called upon to provide, and which were not specified or measured in the original contract documents, must be paid for. Before admitting these extra charges the engineer should investigate their causes. Special costs that result from the failure of a sub-contractor to execute the work properly, or his delay in carrying out the work, are not chargeable to the employer, and must be recovered by the contractor from the sub-contractor. For instance, if a metal lined bore-hole of considerable depth took twice the time forecast to complete because the metal liners originally provided were defective, and consequently increased the charges for crane hire and temporary staging, then the sub-contractor would be liable.

The contractor will be entitled to be paid for the attendance he provides for firms employed directly by the promoter, but he can only ask for profit on the value of this work when the contract bills originally included items for the work to be carried out by the contractor or nominated sub-contractors. In such cases the contractor will be entitled to a profit on the value of the work carried out by the firm employed direct, equivalent to what he would have received if no variation had occurred. The same rule will apply when works in the contract are carried out by the employer's own organization. The profit must be calculated on the notional value of the work.

When a nominated sub-contractor defaults and has to be replaced by another sub-contractor the engineer or architect is under a duty to renominate within a reasonable time.[1] The renomination process often causes delay to the main contractor and involves the contractor in additional costs, which are not

---

[1] *Percy Bilton Ltd.* v. *G.L.C.* (1982) 1 W.L.R. 794.

recoverable when there is no reasonable delay in the appointment of a new sub-contractor.

There may also be the problem of making good defects in the work carried out by the original sub-contractor before he was replaced. In *Fairclough Building Ltd. v. Rhuddlan B.C.*[1] it was held that as the main contractor had neither the right nor the responsibility to carry out the prime cost work himself[2] he could not be liable for the defective work of the defaulting sub-contractor prior to practical completion. But after the completion of the works the contractor would be liable for the defective work of the defaulting sub-contractor, as he was responsible to rectify all defects due to defective materials and workmanship including those of his nominated sub-contractors. However, the main contractor is not responsible for defective work because of deficiencies in the design work by the nominated sub-contractor.

Dayworks

The I.C.E. contract permits the engineer to "order in writing that any substitute or additional work shall be executed on a daywork basis" if in his opinion it is necessary or desirable. Under what conditions are dayworks necessary or desirable? Only when the normal processes of measurement and valuation are not practicable. It is possible to measure almost every operation undertaken on a civil engineering site, and differences of opinion occur as to whether or not valuation of the measured item is practicable. But if the items do not fall within the general sequence of operations and require long and cumbersome descriptions when measured, it would be normal for them to be dealt with on a daywork basis. If the bills did not contain a daywork schedule,[3] the contractor must be paid at the

---

[1] [1983] CILL 41.

[2] *T.A. Bickerton & Sons Ltd.* v. *N.W.M.R.H.B.* [1970] 1 W.L.R. 607.

[3] See Chapter 4, p. 92.

rate and prices and in accordance with the conditions of the *Schedules of Dayworks carried out Incidental to Contract Work*. With this schedule, the net amount of "wages" which is defined as wages, bonus, travelling and tool allowance, and all prescribed payments in respect of time lost due to inclement weather. The rates must be those prescribed in the current Working Rule Agreement of the Civil Engineering Construction Conciliation Board or other appropriate wage-fixing authority and, where no rates are prescribed by a wage-fixing body, the actual payments made to the workmen concerned. A percentage (133 per cent in 1983) is added to the net amount of wages for the various statutory payments, holiday pay, site supervision and staff, small tools, protective clothing, etc., and head office charges and profit. Site supervision and staff will include the agent, general foremen, timekeepers and clerks. Materials are charged at the invoice price including all cash discounts not exceeding 2½ per cent to which is added a percentage (12½ per cent in 1983). The schedule contains hire rates for standard items of plant applicable to the contractor's plant already on the site, profit and overheads are included in the rates, but percentages are added to the listed hire rates from time to time to bring the rates in line with the continued increase in all costs associated with plant. Plant hirer's accounts have the same percentage addition as materials added. Labour only sub-contractors' accounts, including those for plant operators, have a separate percentage addition (64 per cent in 1983). Plant hire rates normally include fuel and consumable stores, but are exclusive of the wages of operators and attendants.

Problems commonly arise in the interpretation of the schedules' application. If only a portion of the day is spent on daywork, the charge for travelling time should be proportional to the hours spent on daywork. The price of materials obtained from the builder's stock may include justifiable charges for handling and storage; but the total cost should not exceed the market price for a similar quantity of the same materials. Profit may be charged on the notional value of materials supplied by the employer, but no allowance can be made for cash discount.

The daywork sheets must always record the names and trades of the operatives, and show the daily hours worked, and the value of travelling expenses; bonus or plus rates should always be given separately. There should always be a description of the work on each sheet, giving details of location, extent of work, and the reason why it was required. The materials consumed and plant employed should be recorded periodically on separate sheets. The I.C.E. contract states that the dayworks should be delivered daily to the engineer's representative. This rule is often not observed. The resident engineer must decide whether or not it is necessary to enforce it. If he is wise he will not allow delivery of the sheets to be delayed beyond a few days at the most.

According to the I.C.E. contract dayworks can only be rendered after the engineer has ordered in writing that the additional or substituted work can be carried out on such a basis. This will not deter the contractor from rendering dayworks for items not yet authorized, even when he knows it is probable that sanction will not be given to payment on that basis. He will claim that the sheets will provide an authentic record of the cost upon which the measured valuation can be based. The engineer, although he may not consider daywork payment is justified, is at liberty to accept them as record sheets. Signature of the record sheets by the engineer is recommended, provided the numbers are kept to reasonable proportions. Daywork and record sheets should be carefully perused at the time of submission, and a note made as to which variation order they apply. When the engineer is of the opinion that the sheets will be made redundant by measurement, or are covered by items in the bills of quantities, he should record this for future discussion with the contractor. The reasonableness of the time charged should also be considered, and a check made on the quantities of materials used. The time is seldom easy to assess, but by inspecting the work as it progresses, its relative accuracy can be controlled. The corroboration of the quantities of materials should not be difficult, and a tendency to undercharge materials is sometimes met with. The engineer should rectify deficiencies with the same zeal that he would use to reduce excess charges.

Fluctuations

When the price variation clause is operative, the contractor must give, as soon as possible, written notice of any decrease or increase in the wages of the operatives or market price of items on the basic list. The risks associated with movements in wage rates and material prices are transferred from the contractor to the employer, and it is important that the contractor always fulfils this obligation to inform the employer of price movements. Sometimes by variation the engineer may be able to limit the extra cost resulting from an increase in material prices. In the unlikely event of a fall in the price of steel being concurrent with a steep rise in the price of cement, it may be possible, by modifying the design, to dampen down the effect of the price increase. Usually, movements in material prices are not sufficiently significant to justify alterations to the specification or design, especially if the work is already in progress.

The net increase of site wages must be allowed together with any increases in the contribution made by the contractor to National Insurance, occupational insurance, or holidays with pay. The consequential increases in the cost of employer's liability and third party insurance allowed for in the J.C.T. contract cannot be recovered when the I.C.E. contract is used. The I.C.E. contract should be amended to allow the contractor to recoup these additional costs when the contract is of exceptionally long duration.

Wage increases for men employed by the contractor at his plant yard or workshops can only be allowed when the men are directly employed upon the contract work, and provision has been made for an accurate record of the time occupied on different contracts to be kept. Claims based on a percentage formula should not be conceded. It must be acknowledged that an accurate allocation of yard and workshop costs to individual contracts is often impracticable. When movements in yard, or workshop labour costs, are likely to be of importance the alternatives of excluding such claims entirely or the provision of a formula for their calculation should be considered, and the contract conditions worded accordingly. The same considerations are applicable to the wage increases of lorry drivers.

The increases of labour costs accruing as a result of non-productive overtime are not explicitly mentioned in either the J.C.T. or I.C.E. fluctuations clauses. It is recommended that these increases should be allowed even for unauthorized non-productive overtime on all contracts, as there is no logical reason for discriminating against them. Where government departments or local authorities are concerned, the procedure must be agreed with the responsible officers. Sometimes permission to allow these costs is refused, although the grounds on which refusal is justified are not easy to comprehend.

The courts have held that the fluctuation clause in the J.C.T. contract does not allow the contractor to recover increases in wages paid under a bonus incentive scheme *voluntarily* introduced by him, even when such a scheme is geared to basic wage rates and of a type approved and encouraged by the National Joint Council for the Building Industry. The increases in wages comprehended by the clause are those which the contractor is *compelled* to pay by reason of decisions of the N.J.C.[1]

The basic prices of materials and fuel entered in the schedule should have been scrutinized and checked before the contract was signed, and where necessary the contractor should have been requested to support his price by a quotation or an invoice. Sometimes the contractor will price materials at below the current market rates. These rates should be allowed to stand if it can be shown that he is able to purchase materials at favourable rates becuase of bulk-purchasing agreements or for other reasons. Unfortunately a contractor does not always succeed in buying materials at the reduced rates quoted. Whether or not he is successsful the adjustment should be based on the difference between the market price at the date of tender and time of purchase. For it would seem proper that the contractor should retain any gain or carry any loss resulting from the enterprise of his buying department, or his opportunities for bulk-purchase.

---

[1] *William Sindall Ltd.* v. *North West Thames Regional Health Authority* [1977] I.C.R. 294.

It will be found that the above recommendations will lose their theoretical simplicity when applied in practice to the assessment of the fluctuation in the cost of materials for which there is no readily identifiable market rate. Timber prices, both for hardwood and softwood, illustrate the problems involved in their most complex form. Average market prices are quoted for various grades and qualities of hardwoods and softwoods. But the idea of a market price for a single consignment of timber is illusory. The price of timber bought at the docks will be influenced by the average quality of the planks or logs, the classification of which will depend upon the skill and judgement of the buyer and the current relationship of supply to demand. The invoice may including kilning, conversion, and haulage costs which were not an element in the original quotation. Faced with these difficulties the contractor and the engineer should agree on adjustments to be based on a hypothetical average market value. The price of paint and other manufactured materials not the subject of a price maintenance agreement have no common market price. The acceptance of the price movements of the materials of the manufacturer chosen by the contractor will solve this difficulty so long as the basic price and all the materials are obtained from the same source.

Further troubles may be a consequence of the basic price being based on a different method of packaging the material from that eventually chosen. Cement may have been priced for delivery in bulk containers, and actually purchased in bags. The correct procedure is to allow the difference between the cost of the bagged cement at the time of tender and date of purchase. Any saving or excess resulting from the use of alternative packaging would be absorbed by the contractor, unless the change was brought about by a variation ordered by the engineer. Then the difference in price would be dealt with by fixing a new rate for the varied work. Adjustments should never be made under this clause for differences between the cost of materials purchased in bulk and in small quantities. Like must be compared with like. Again the contractor must bear any difference in cost resulting from a different method of purchasing, variations excepted. Variations in material prices due to the engineer's instructions must always be dealt with by measurement and rate fixing. The contractor can only recover the net increase of cost under the price variation clause; while when new rates are fixed he is entitled to his additional profit as well. Materials taken from the contractor's store should be allowed at current market rates, and the original price paid together with storage and handling should not be taken into account. Handling and storage may of course be charged if they are the consequence of an engineer's instruction.

It is sometimes argued that the contractor is not entitled to the increase in cost of materials and labour that accrue solely because a portion of the work is carried out after the completion date, or extended completion date. It would seem equitable to refuse payment on these grounds. Nevertheless, the I.C.E. contract gives no explicit guidance on this point, and it is suggested that the bill of quantities should make it quite clear whether or not such payments will be allowed. Similar considerations affect the payment of increased costs in relation to the making good of defects during the maintenance period. Fluctuations are corrections adjusted by reference to indices published by the National Economic Development Office.[1]

Rate-fixing

During the preparation of the draft remeasurement account, or on its completion, new rates will be required for those items in the remeasurement bills which were not contained in the original bills. The I.C.E. contract prescribes that these rates must be fixed by the engineer. Should these rates be unacceptable to the contractor he can incorporate them in a claim. So that disagreement and claims can be reduced to a minimum it is normal practice for the engineer or his quantity surveyor and the contractor to meet, discuss and agree all the

---

[1] NEDO Indices for various sections of the construction industry. Not less than two series are in existence.

new rates in the variation or remeasurement bills. The engineer can fix rates and offer the priced bills to the contractor for scrutiny and approval before the meeting, or the rate-fixing can be undertaken by the contractor; the engineer then reviews these prices. Some argue that the contractor is better equipped, in view of his practical knowledge of costs, to carry out the initial rate-fixing, and the engineer when reviewing the contractor's prices should devote his energies to reducing those he considers too high. Others claim that it is more in keeping with the contract when the engineer fixes the new rates on a theoretical basis, and the contractor need only assemble the information he needs to give factual support to his claim for revision of those rates which he belives are below their true value. The engineer must decide which method is to be adopted.

The items for which rates are to be fixed can be classified as follows:

1. Items to be priced *pro rata* to the contract rates.
2. Items to be priced at rates based on new build-ups consistent with the original method of rate-fixing.
3. Items to be priced at rates based on the original bill-rates but revised to take account of the altered nature of work, or conditions under which it is carried out.

Rate-fixing for the first group is comparatively simple, when new rates are obtainable by taking the arithmetical averages of two or more bill prices. In the example which follows, the new rates are shown in **bold type**:

Portland cement concrete $(20N/mm^2)$

In walls 150 mm thick	100 m²	£10.00
In walls 200 mm thick	90 m²	**£13.34**
In walls 225 mm thick	120 m²	**£15.00**
In walls 250 mm thick	170 m²	£16.65
In walls 300 mm thick	80 m²	£18.25
In walls 300 mm thick	200 m²	£55.00

Such straightforward arithmetical computations from an inspection of the orginal rates will not necessarily give the correct answer. It is apparent from the original pricing of the above example that no allowance has been made for the increase in the cost of placing as the thickness of the wall or slab reduces. Had the original bills contained prices only for 150 mm and 300 mm thick walls it would be reasonable to assume that the placing costs of a cubic metre of concrete increased in ratio to the reduction of wall thickness. The first step in establishing the price of the 225 mm wall would be the ascertainment of the value of a cubic metre of concrete in both 150 mm and 300 mm thick walls:

		£
1 m³ in wall, 150 mm thick = £10.00 × 6⅔ =		66.66
1 m³ in wall, 300 mm thick = £18.25 × 3⅓ =		60.83
Extra cost of placing in walls 150 mm thick		£5.83 m³

Therefore the rates for the 200 mm and 225 mm walls would be obtained as follows:

	£
225 mm wall = ¾ × £18.25 =	13.69
Extra cost of placing = £5.83 × .225 =	1.31
	£15.00 m³

	£
200 mm wall = ⅔ × £18.25 =	12.17
Extra cost of placing = £5.83 × .200 =	1.17
	£13.34

The contrasting rates obtained exemplify the rule that the pattern of pricing used in the original bills and schedules must be followed when new rates are fixed. This will remain true despite the fact that an engineer may consider the original rate pattern does not accord with generally accepted views about cost relationships. When a new price must be fixed by extrapolation, further caution is required, as the price gradient can fluctuate as certain critical depths and sizes are reached.

The following example is based on the assumption that the ground to be excavated at the greater depth is of a similar character to that at the shallower levels:

Excavate for pier holes exceeding 2 m and

		£
not exceeding 5 m deep	m³	25.00
Ditto exceeding 5 m and not exceeding 10 m deep	m³	28.50
Ditto exceeding 10 m and not exceeding 15 m deep	m³	37.21

The new rate has been fixed by allowing an additional 1/10th of an hour for one labourer, a banksman, and an excavator and operator, and one 1/20th of an hour for two timbermen. The calculation is shown below:

			£
Labourer	1/10th of £4.00	=	0.40
Banksman	1/10th of £4.30	=	0.43
Excavator operator	1/10th of £4.50	=	0.45
Timberman	2/20th of £4.30	=	0.43
			1.71
Overheads etc.	12½ per cent	= say	0.21
			1.92
Excavator	1/10th of £60.00		6.00
			£7.92
Add profit 10 per cent			£0.79
			£8.71
Bill item as above			28.50
			£37.21

In practice the ground is often more difficult to dig at greater depth either because of its increased density or because the digging is below the level of the water table, or the surcharge on less cohesive strata may result in heavy increases in timbering costs. The second class of items for which rates must be fixed are those for which no comparable rates appear in the bills, and a new build-up is required. The procedure will be that used for fixing the original rates described in a previous chapter with the proviso that the percentage additions for profit and overheads must follow the pattern of the original pricing, and the contractor's consideration of the price will be influenced by his cost record of the operation involved.

The third type of rate-fixing, where the nature or conditions of the work have altered, usually concerns those matters which are often the subject of claims, and are better dealt with in association with such claims.

Claims

Mention has been made of claims in connection with interim payments. Apart from claims for damages for breach of the contract, the contractor under the I.C.E. contract may be able to make a claim under one or more of the many provisions of the contract which entitle him to claims for additional loss and expense. In particular, claims might be made under Clause 12 in respect of adverse physical conditions or Clause 52 (4) for variations. The object of Clause 12 is to protect the contractor from disproportionate risks, provided it could not be expected that they would be foreseen by an experienced contractor. For instance, should adverse conditions (other than weather conditions or conditions due to weather conditions) be encountered, or artificial obstructions met with, which the contractor considers will involve additional work or the use of additional plant, he must give notice in writing of his intention to make a claim. If feasible, the claim must be supported by a firm estimate of the cost, and when not so supported, an approximate estimate must be given. Improved efficiency of site investigation in recent years should make the need for such claims less likely than in the past. Nevertheless, site investigation is essentially a sampling process, and there will be occasions which make it necessary for this clause to be invoked.

The I.C.E. conditions of contract envisage that the contractor is not responsible for the design of the permanent works and therefore it has been doubted whether Clause 12 can be invoked when the design as well as the construction is the responsibility of the contractor. Much will depend upon which party carries out and takes responsibility for the site investigations. In some cases it may be held that if the employer carried out the investigation and provided the information upon which the contractor based his design, the employer implicitly warrants that the information is accurate. In such a case the contractor, although without a remedy under Clause 12, would be entitled to reimbursement for extra expenses incurred by way of damages for breach of warranty.[1] Disagreement between the engineer and the contractor on the validity of a claim will sometimes occur. There can be no hard and fast rules for recognizing conditions that give obvious grounds for making a claim, although an alteration in conditions which necessitated the redesign of the permanent construction would give grounds for making a claim about which there could be little argument. Artesian water pressures exerted within a cofferdam which demanded the abandonment of a cofferdam constructed of sheet steel piles and the substitution of pneumatic caissons[2] offer an obvious example.

The extra work required as a result of either artificial obstructions or unforeseen physical conditions will be measured and valued in accordance with routine procedure. It is the extra costs involved that cannot be covered by bill rates that would be the subject of a claim. Breaking out old concrete would be paid for at the scheduled rates; if the additional quantities encountered are small, the contractor would have no claim for additional expense. But if considerable quantities must be broken out and compel a different approach to the job, and the use of alternative plant, there will be case for a claim.

---

[1] *Bacal Construction (Midlands) Ltd.* v. *Northampton Development Corporation* (1975) 8 B.L.R. 88.

[2] Széchy, *Foundation Failures.*

Having decided he is entitled to make a claim for additional payment the contractor, when he gives written notice to the engineer, must specify the conditions and obstructions met with in some detail, and give particulars of the additional work and plant required. At the same time he must give an estimate of the anticipated delay, and the amount of interference with the execution of the works. This notice must be given as soon as possible. If the contractor fails to give the proper notices or particulars then he shall only be entitled to payment to the extent that the engineer has not been prevented from investigating the claim because of this failure. The claim must be supported by either a firm or an approximate estimate of the extra costs. The engineer should investigate the claim on receipt of the notice. He has four courses open to him:

(a) Admit any of the facts and circumstances.
(b) Give such suspension under Clause 40, or variation order under Clause 51, as may be appropriate in the circumstances including, if he thinks fit, an order to vary the works so as to avoid the necessity for doing the additional work or using the constructional plant.
(c) Accept the estimate of cost and admit the employer's liability.
(d) Accept the estimate of cost without admitting the employer's liability so that no obligation is imposed on the employer unless and until liability is either admitted or established.

Whichever course is decided upon, it will have no validity unless notified in writing. When the contractor does not give a firm quotation, or the engineer rejects it, regular returns of the costs incurred in connection with the claim must be rendered by the contractor. Normally, these will be rendered on daywork sheets, although their costing will not necessarily be the same as that used for dayworks. The isolation of these extra costs is not always practicable, and the whole cost of the operation must be recorded, and a deduction made for the value of the measurable work and other items included in the contract cost. Sometimes the lack of correlation between cost and contract price will make this method unreliable. Failure to agree on such claims can be settled by arbitration. The contractor must comply strictly with the procedure set out in Clause 12, otherwise he may find that he cannot put forward a claim. It was found by an arbitrator adjudicating on a claim for about £12,000[1] that the conditions met with in the construction of a sea-wall justified the contractor's claim, but a judge's ruling was asked for on the claim because of the failure of the contractor to give the required notices. The judge held that the failure to fulfil the procedure required by clause 12 barred the engineer or the arbitrator from considering the claim.[2] But this ruling would usually only apply when the result of failure to give proper notice of the claim is to prevent or substantially prejudice the investigation of the claim by the engineer.[3]

Linked with claims arising from this clause is the practicability of the engineer's design. The courts have given a restricted interpretation, however, to the expression "engineer's design". In one case, for example, contractors entered into a contract with a local authority employer, in I.C.E. form, for laying new sewers. In the course of the work an old sewer, which the contractors knew was at least 100 years old, and which lay under an embankment upon which was a main road, had to be crossed. The contractors could expect to meet the old sewer anywhere under the embankment, and in fact the heading for the new sewer met the filled-in original heading for the old sewer under the road. Water and silt came into the heading from the old sewer, which had fractures where the earth surrounding it was disturbed, and as a result the road became blocked. Substantial cost was incurred in putting the matter right. The court held that the condition found by the contractors was not due to the "engineer's design", which meant the plan showing the precise nature of the work to be carried out, but was a condition which could have been

---

[1] About £90,000 at 1977 values.

[2] *Blackford & Son (Calne) Ltd.* v. *Christchurch Corporation* (1962) 60 L.G.R. 214, The *Times*, 16 March.

[3] I.C.E. Clause 52 (4) (e).

reasonably foreseen by an experienced contractor, so that, under the terms of the contract, the contractors had to take the risk upon themselves.[1] Sometimes it will be possible to introduce some safeguard from such claims by incorporating alternative procedures to meet special conditions. Provisional quantities in the bills give the contractor an opportunity to price items carried out under conditions differing from those expected, and a measure of protection is offered to both parties should the worst occur.

Claims arising from disagreement over the measurement and valuation of the contract work are dealt with in Clause 52 (4) of the I.C.E. contract. In connection with these and the extra costs covered by Clause 12, new rates must be fixed for items, the rates of which must be adjusted because of the altered nature of the work. A tunnel for a sewer to be lined with pre-cast concrete ring-linings had manholes sited at 30 m intervals on the contract drawings. The engineer instructed them to be placed at 60 m intervals after the acceptance of the tender. The contractor had priced the item of excavation and timbering for the tunnel at £66.50 per m^3 which was computed on the basis of an average haul of 7.5 m linear to shafts formed by the permanent manholes. As a result of the variation, the average haul was, instead, 15 m linear. The contractor claimed higher rates for both excavation and linings. The engineer's calculations for a single length of tunnel containing 5,700 m^3 of excavation and 4,600 m^2 of concrete linings were as shown below:

Extra cost of hauling per m^3 of excavation

	£
Cost of monorail, say	0.25
Cost of power wagon 2½ min at £5.50 per hr, say ..	0.23
Two labourers at 16p per m^3	0.32
	0.80
Add 10 per cent, say	0.08
	£0.88
Original rate for excavation and timbering	59.00
Adjusted rate for excavation and timbering	£59.88

[1] *C.J. Pearce & Co. Ltd.* v. *Hereford Corporation* [1968] 66 L.G.R. 647.

Extra cost per m² of concrete linings	£
Cost of monorail (included with excavation)	–
Cost of power wagon, 1 min at £5.50 per hr, say	0.09
Two labourers at 10 p per m²	0.10
	0.19
Add 10 per cent, say	0.02
	0.21
Original rate for concrete linings	39.00
	£39.21

The extra payment due to the contractor at these adjusted rates would have been:

	£
5,700 m³ at £0.88	5016.00
4,600 m² at £0.21	966.00
	£5,982.00

The contractor was not satisfied with these rates and claimed the following sum which was calculated from the cost records submitted to the engineer:

	£	£
100 m monorail at £2.00 for 30 days		60.00
500 hr power wagon at £6.00 per hr ..		3000.00
600 hr labourer at £4.50 per hr	2700	
Add 20 per cent	540	3240.00
		£6300.00

Should the engineer be satisfied that the cost record is correct, he can accept the contractor's figures, and adjust his own calculations. When he is of the opinion that the contractor's cost record is incorrect, he must give the contractor his reasons for this opinion. The contractor, unless he can prove the engineer wrong, should accept the engineer's new rates, the onus of proof being placed on the contractor.

Any claim made should be within the terms of the contract. Opinions will differ on whether peripheral matters are within the terms of the contract. Obviously if the claim relates to weather conditions or other matters at the risk of the contractor, he will have no obvious grounds for a claim. Nevertheless, he will sometimes make a claim although the contract makes no provision for it, in the belief that its consideration is a matter of fairness and equity. Such applications are called *ex gratia* claims, and any payments would be a voluntary act, and not in fulfilment of the employer's contractual duty. Contractual claims can be settled by the engineer without reference to the employer, unless they arise from the employer's direct interference. The engineer has no authority to settle *ex gratia* claims, and he must obtain the employer's decision on them. The engineer will generally be expected to given an opinion on the merits of the claim. It has not been unknown for contractual claims to be admitted by the employer on an *ex gratia* basis. By these means the employer has the satisfaction of knowing he has not conceded or waived his contractual rights, while the contractor receives some reimbursement.

The J.C.T. contract provides for the contractor to make written application for any direct loss or expense not reimbursable under the contract rules for valuation and payment, and attributable to a variation or disturbance of the regular progress of the works caused by the employer or his agents. Although the I.C.E. contract does not explicitly limit claims to direct losses, it is doubtful whether other losses could be claimed. Neither the engineer nor the arbitrator could settle such a point. It would be a matter for legal argument, although the employer could make an *ex gratia* payment for indirect losses if he considered the contractor had some justification for his claim.

Clause 9 (2) in the GC/Works/1 contract allows for the payment of properly incurred expenses, beyond those provided for in the contract, which arise from the superintending officer's instructions. Expenses incurred following instructions for the suspension of the works to avoid risk of damage from frost and like causes are excluded. It also allows for the deduction from the contract sum of savings for the same reasons. Neither the J.C.T. contract nor GC/Works/1 explicitly permit the contractor to claim expenses consequent on his meeting with adverse physical conditions or artificial obstructions which could not have been reasonably foreseen by an experienced contractor.

Settlement of the Final Account

Under the I.C.E. contract the contractor shall submit a statement of final account and supporting documentation to the engineer not later than three months after the date of the maintenance certificate. The engineer shall issue a final certificate within three months of receipt of the final account and of all information reasonably required for its verification.

The account should, if possible, be agreed at each stage of its preparation or at the completion of each section. When this is not possible a draft account should be sent to the contractor for his agreement. It should show the final sum that the engineer proposes to certify, but will be subject to amendment by agreement in the course of negotiations. When the contractor is dilatory in supplying the engineer with p.c. invoices, price variation claims, and other information, the only remedy is to submit an incomplete account to the contractor with a request for prompt action.

When an agreed final figure is reached, the contractor should be required to issue a statement confirming the amount, and certifying that he has no further claims in relation to the contract. When the final certificate is issued, the engineer should report to the employer upon any differences between the contract sum and the final sum. The engineer should peruse the account with the object of discovering whether he could give the facts relating to every variation from the original contract bills and schedules, making such notes as he considers advisable during his examination. Sometimes he will also make an analysis of the additional sum expended. The employer will usually be interested to know of both extras and savings which come about because of the fresh instructions he issued after the completion of the tender documents. He may also require detailed analysis of the expenditure incurred to aid him when planning future projects, or to assist him in the allocation of the capital cost for auditing and costing. Where possible, the engineer should endeavour to obtain from the employer information on the purposes for which he requires the analysis, so that the figures required can be obtained without further investigation.

CHAPTER 11

MANAGEMENT AND SETTLEMENT OF COST REIMBURSEMENT CONTRACTS

Cost Control

"Provided the contractor's remuneration for the carrying out of the work is fixed and provided there is no excessive remuneration payable to him in respect of plant employed, the interests of the building owner and the contractor in carrying out the work efficiently and with economy appear to be analogous." These words taken from the Simon Report[1] are equally applicable to a civil engineering project carried out on a cost basis. The making good of defects must not however be chargeable to the cost, but should be paid for out of the contractor's profits. The chief danger to be avoided in a contract of this kind is the deterioration of the attitude of both site management and men towards economy and efficiency resulting from the absence of a system of valuation independent of the cost, against which they can compare their efforts. The accounting system employed should not only ascertain the sums due to the contractor, but also provide the contractor's head office and the engineer with an effective instrument for checking the reasonableness of the cost incurred in relation to the work carried out. One method that can be employed is to separate the cost of different operations and sections of the work, and compare these costs with valuations based on approximate quantities. The effectiveness of this form of

[1] *The Placing and Management of Building Contracts* (Simon Report) p. 37, H.M.S.O.

control will depend on the accuracy of the allocations made, and gangers and charge hands must spend time in making returns. Some degree of control can also be exercised by the use of progress charts which indicate the time allowed for an operation and the number of men to be employed upon it.

The engineer as a matter of policy should have the right to comment upon and scrutinize the contractor's schemes for the organization of the work, and upon his choice and siting of plant, but he should endeavour to confine himself to questions on the proposed schemes, and avoid direct innovations and alterations to the proposals made by the contractor. Properly trained cost clerks must be employed at the site to record the cost, and keep a check on the purchase of materials and use of plant. The engineer must make arrangements for the cost to be checked on the employer's behalf, and if no member of his own staff is qualified to do this he would be well advised to employ a quantity surveyor. The system of recording expenditure and presenting the accounts should be agreed before the contract starts. In all cases the contractor should keep separate books for entering the costs, and when large sums are involved separate banking accounts are sometimes opened through which all income and expenditure is transmitted. The engineer can reserve the right to approve the persons appointed as storekeepers, timekeepers, clerks and accountants. The contract should contain a schedule listing in detail all the items that are chargeable to the cost, and the amount of the fixed fee. The fixed fee will normally exclude the value of work executed by nominated sub-contractors to which a percentage fee will be added. The amount of the fixed fee will be obtained by applying a percentage to the estimated value of the work. If all site charges are included in the cost then the fee will represent head office costs and profit. A reasonable fee for civil engineering work will be based on a percentage between 10 and 15 per cent for small works, and from 10 to 5 per cent for large contracts. Fees based on a percentage of 2 or 3 per cent are on record. Should the head office of the contractors be responsible for some of the design work then a higher fee should be agreed. It may be more convenient to break down the estimated value of the contract and apply different percentages to those sections of the works for which the contractor's head office will incur varying design and drawing office services. When the contract includes the design of mechanical plant and pipe work comparatively heavy head offices charges will be incurred. Also, if hand tools, ladders and similar equipment are excluded from the cost, the percentage on which the fixed fee is based should be adjusted.

Labour

The engineer should have the right to approve the rates of wages and other emoluments paid to the operatives, and, when these are in excess of the rates approved in the working rule agreements, they should be comparable with those paid on other sites in the same area. On exceptionally isolated sites there will be no possibility of making a comparison, and sometimes special payments will be required to attract men to the site. Housing will be required, and amenities must be provided to console the men for the absence of urban amusements during their leisure hours. It is the custom in some areas of the African and Asian continents to take the whole family on the pay roll, and provision must be made for housing and feeding them all, while it is desirable that medical and welfare services should be available. The number of men employed upon the site will be within the contractor's control, but the engineer should have the right to comment if he is of the opinion that too many or too few workmen are on the strength. It should be remembered that the assessment of labour requirements calls for considerable experience and judgement in the balancing of needs of peak periods and with those of slack periods. No foreman will dismiss or transfer first class workmen even when he knows he will not be able to employ them at full capacity for several weeks, if there is little hope of obtaining replacements at a later date. Neither will he be inclined to expand a labour force so that for one short period a single operation can be carried out expeditiously. Nevertheless these difficulties should not inhibit the engineer from expressing his views when the labour force is obviously disproportionate to requirements. The allocation of payments made for National Insurance and holidays with pay contribution when operatives are employed on a site for only part of a week should be dealt with on a similar basis to that used when fluctuation claims are made.[1] The cost of the wages of men employed at the contractor's yard or works should not be allowed on a percentage basis. If it is impossible for the contractor to allocate the cost, then no payment for this labour cost should be allowed, but the price negotiated for the plant and materials involved should cover the cost of the off-site labour.

Plant

The basis on which the cost of plant is to be assessed should be agreed before the contract is entered into, and the method of valuation incorporated in the contract conditions. On large contracts of long duration it may be that the best course will be for new plant to be bought, and at the end of the contract, or when the plant is no longer required upon the site, the contractor can either allow a credit for its residual use or it can be sold. This system can be used for both the acquisition of mechanical plant, and the purchase of equipment such as ladders, barrows, hand tools, scaffolding, and forms for concrete, provided these items form part of the prime cost.

Usually the plant and equipment will be drawn from the contractor's store, and it should be paid for in accordance with the terms agreed before the contract was entered into. Another method is for arrangements to be made for the purchase of plant belonging to the contractor, and for its repurchase by him when it is no longer needed for the contract. Opinions differ on the advisability or the need to distinguish between standing and operating time when all fuel, power and consumable stores are chargeable to the contract. It is true that when plant is in use a

[1] See Chapter 10, pp. 215–6.

slightly higher rate may be justified because of the wear and tear on working parts; on the other hand the difficulty of keeping accurate records that separate working time from standing time may justify the use of a common rate for both. The average ratio between standing and operating time for different types of plant is ascertainable. Some of the plant may be hired, and competitive quotations should be obtained for the more expensive hired items. When comparing such quotations the term offered should be compared as well as the price. Maintenance and service should be included in the cost, and the time the plant is out of commission as a result of breakdown should not be chargeable.

When scaffolding and similar equipment is hired, arrangements should be made for a reduced hire charge after a given period; if this is not done it is possible that the employer's payments for hire will exceed the cost of purchasing the scaffolding or equipment outright.

Materials

Whether materials are ordered and purchased through the head-office buying department or by the site management will be a matter for the contractor's decision. Materials required in large quantities should be the subject of competitive estimates and except for items of trivial value the quotations of suppliers should be subject to the approval of the engineer or the quantity surveyor. The promoter should have the benefit of discounts, rebates, credits and allowances made, excepting only a cash discount of 2½ per cent. A programme linked to the master chart should be prepared for the purchase of all materials, because it is important that all materials should be available when required without prolonged storage being necessary. Premature delivery of materials to the site may result in deterioration and breakages; furthermore money can be fruitlessly expended in the transference of materials from one part of the site to another. A trained man should be responsible when materials are ordered at the site. Materials for which only a limited space is available or which should not be stored for long periods can be ordered on a daily basis by the agent, if arrangements have been made previously with the supplier that these orders will be fulfilled on demand for an agreed price. It is suggested that materials supplied by the promoter should be invoiced and paid for in the normal way. The accountancy required for the transaction will act as a cost control, and must not be considered as a piece of redundant book-keeping. Materials requirements can usually be predicted with accuracy, and a thorough and continuous check should be kept on the quantities used. Over-ordering is the most likely cause of unnecessary waste, because once the materials arrive on the site the surplus is usually not discovered until late in the contract, by which time the unneeded materials have suffered damage. Often the cost of collecting these materials together and returning them to store outweighs their residual value.

Sub-contracts

Nominated sub-contracts should be dealt with on the same principles used for a measure and value contract. Work which the engineer has agreed can be sub-let need not be valued on a cost basis. In fact wherever possible these sub-traded portions of the work should be the subject of competitive tenders based on a schedule of prices, and the work should be measured on completion. The question of the effect of the value of the sub-let work on the contractor's fee has given cause for debate. Normally the cost of sub-let work, which will include a profit for the sub-contractor, will be no greater than the net cost that would have been incurred had the contractor's own workmen been employed. But to save argument and doubt it is advisable that the sections of the work to be sub-let should be scheduled and agreed with the engineer during the pre-contract negotiations and before the fixed fee is established. The sub-contractor's schedules of prices, or the terms under which he will charge his work at cost should be submitted to the engineer for his approval. The engineer should not only satisfy himself that the price is reasonable, but should also ensure that the terms and conditions are clarified because any additional

charges made by the sub-contractor due to the ambiguity of the
the terms will be paid for by the employer.

Valuations

Interim payments will normally be at monthly intervals.
Labour costs can be taken direct from the wages sheets. The
approximate value of the materials can be obtained by
abstracting the quantities of the main materials from the
material record sheets. The prices for the materials should be
obtained from the quotations, or when these are not available,
the average market price should be used. Nominated sub-
contractors should be dealt with in a way no different from that
used for measurement contracts. A proportion of the fixed fee
should be paid each month. Retention should be deducted in
accordance with the contract conditions. The approximate
monthly valuations should be superseded by an accurate and
detailed account. The period covered by each account is a
matter for agreement between the contractor and the engineer.
It is suggested that the period for an account should not exceed
four months, and monthly accounts can be prepared if required.
There should not be undue delay between the presentation of
the account and the end of the accountancy period.

The monthly valuation will provide an opportunity for the
cost controls previously mentioned to be exercised, and a
review of progress in relation to cost to be made. The valuation
can be analysed to obtain the expenditure on each section of the
work; and the relative expenditure on labour, plant, and
materials can be compared. If these are not in the expected
ratios, the reasons for the deviations from the norm should be
sought, and if necessary, uneconomic procedures corrected.

Adjustment of the Fixed Fee

The fixed fee will be based upon the original estimated cost of
the work. When variations occur, an estimate of their effect on
the final cost should be made, and when the difference between

the original estimated cost and the final estimated cost is significant, an adjustment should be made to the fixed fee. Alterations to the value of p.c. sums will normally have no effect on the fixed fee as a percentage for profit is normally added to these sums, and the actual increase or decrease in work carried out by the principal contractor in connection with the nominated firm's work is usually not of sufficient magnitude to justify varying the fixed fee. Each contract, however, must be judged on its own merits.

Direct Labour Contracts

Engineers who serve local authorities will sometimes be concerned with the control of direct labour organizations who undertake repair works and minor alteration schemes. It is not easy to exercise a strict cost control on small works, but several local authorities have successfully instituted systems for the analysis and checking of expenditure upon the repair work carried out by their own organizations. The essential feature of all these schemes is the fixing of targets for all operations. Target fixing should be supplemented by investigation into ways and means of reducing standing time and wasteful procedures.

CHAPTER 12

OVERSEAS CONTRACTS—FINANCE AND PROCEDURES

Finance for Overseas Works

Many of the larger civil engineering projects in developing countries are commissioned by their governments using money from an international creditor.

One of the main sources of such finance is the World Bank which is an Agency of the United Nations Organization providing finance in both developing countries and to a lesser extent elsewhere. The headquarters of the World Bank are in Washington D.C., U.S.A., and its European Offices are in Paris. The World Bank comprises the International Bank for Reconstruction and Development (I.B.R.D.), the International Development Association (I.D.A.) and the International Finance Corporation (I.F.C.). The object of these organizations is to provide investments for projects that will generate wealth, especially in the private sector, within the country borrowing the money while at the same time applying the judgement of a commercial investment banker in appraising a project when making an ordinary loan. Concessional loans for projects in less well-off countries can be made from a special fund.

In Asia the Asian Development Bank (A.D.B.), which is a regional organization sponsored by a group of Asian and Pacific countries, fulfils a similar role to that of the World Bank. The A.D.B. is not a U.N. Organization but has some links with U.N. Agencies.

The problems of the investment banker in assessing the viability of a project before committing a loan should be catered for in the preparation of preliminary or feasibility studies. Such studies should cover both the engineering and economic factors involved and should incorporate reasonably accurate predictions of capital, maintenance and operating costs and realistic programmes.

Financial aid is also provided by individual developed countries but usually such assistance is conditional on the use of that country's designers, contractors or products or on mutual trading arrangements. However, British consulting engineers, unlike those in many other countries, are not subsidized by their government and therefore are able to provide an independent service and are free to specify the most suitable materials for use in overseas projects regardless of their country of origin.

Overseas Forms of Contract

There are many different forms of contract used on overseas construction work but the basis of many of these local contracts and the most widely used standard form is the conditions of contract (International) for Works of Civil Engineering Construction.

An international form of contract based on the fourth edition of the I.C.E. conditions was first introduced in 1956. This document was prepared by the A.C.E. and the Export Group for the Constructional Industries and approved by the Institution of Civil Engineers and is called the Conditions of Contract for Overseas Works Mainly of Civil Engineering Construction and known as the Overseas (Civil) Conditions of Contract.

A similar document was prepared by the Fédération Internationale des Ingénieurs – Conseils (F.I.D.I.C.) and the Fédération Internationale du Bâtiment et des Travaux Publics (F.I.B.T.P.) and the first edition of the Conditions of Contract (International) for Works of Civil Engineering Construction was published in 1957. This document has become known as the

F.I.D.I.C. Contract or the International Conditions of Contract. A second edition was published in 1969 adding headings for clauses for dredging and reclamation work and the third edition was published in 1977. This latest edition incorporates some of the changes made in the fifth edition of the I.C.E. conditions published in 1973 but has still retained much of its fourth edition pedigree.

Unfortunately there are also a number of other standard and hybrid forms of contract in use in various countries, particularly those without involvement in the sponsoring organizations. The introduction of these different forms of contract has generally been in response to the diverse commercial and legal practices in these countries.

The International Conditions of Contract for Civil Engineering are generally unsuitable for overseas building work and multi-discipline projects and hence various substantially amended versions of this contract have been produced for these types of work. These differing and virtually redrafted conditions of contract only create confusion and uncertainty and it is hoped that before long some organization will produce a standard form of contract relevant to overseas building works.

Mechanical and electrical works are covered by the Model Form of General Conditions of Contract for use in connection with Export Contracts (including Delivery to and Erection on Site of Electrical and Mechanical Plant) prepared by the A.C.E., the Institution of Electrical Engineers (I.E.E.) and the Institution of Mechanical Engineers (I.Mech.E.).

Overseas (Civil) Conditions of Contract

The *Overseas (Civil) Conditions of Contract* is still occasionally used. It is also not unknown for the 4th edition of I.C.E. conditions to be used abroad, although it has been superseded in Britain. The clause numbers are in fact identical in both contracts, only a few sub-clauses being different.[1]

---

[1] 4th ed, I.C.E. Conditions of Contract.

Thus Clause 26A in the I.C.E. conditions of contract relating to the duties of employer and contractor under the British Public Utilities Street Works Acts, 1950 is replaced by an extension of Clause 26, stating that the contractor must comply with the local statutes, regulations, etc. of the country where the project is to be carried out. All clauses in the I.C.E. conditions of contract relating to specific English laws and conciliation machinery are either omitted or else replaced by general clauses laying down a principle which could be applied in any country.

Clause 52, dealing with the valuation of variations, has an additional clause in the overseas conditions defining the steps to be taken if variations alter the original contract sum, either up or down, by more than 15 per cent.

The form of tender, form of agreement and appendix are similar, although the appendix of the overseas conditions specifically refers to Clause 66 where it is possible to have the appointer of an arbitrator named in the appendix. If the various parties fail to agree under the I.C.E. conditions, the President of the Institution of Civil Engineers appoints an arbitrator, but as this might not be acceptable in some countries, the alternative is given of agreeing on a different appointer at the time of signing the contract.

A Part II (conditions of particular application) is included and draws attention to certain clauses which may have to be varied or added as necessary to take account of the circumstances and locality of the works. The most important of the additional clauses are:

Clause 70 – *Duties, Dues, etc.* Payment of or relief from customs or other import duties (to be set out in specific terms), harbour, wharfage, landing, pilotage and any other charges or dues.

Clause 71 – *Taxation.* Payment of or exemption from local income or other taxes both as regards the contractor and his staff.

Clause 72 – *Law Governing Contract.* This clause should state the country to the law of which the contract is subject and in accordance with which it will be construed.

Conditions of Contract (International) for Works of Civil Engineering Construction

The third edition of the *Conditions of Contract (International) for Works of Civil Engineering Construction* was published in March 1977. This document has been prepared by F.I.D.I.C. (International Federation of Consulting Engineers) and F.I.E.C. Fédération Internationale Européene de la Construction (European International Federation of Construction) and approved by these organizations together with (I.F.A.W.P.C.A.), the International Federation of Asian and Western Pacific Contractors Associations (F.I.I.C. – La Federacion Interamericana de la Industria de la Construccion – Inter-American Federation for the Construction Industry) and the Associated General Contractors of America (A.G.C.A.) and are recommended by them for general use for contracts for civil engineering construction where tenders are invited on an international basis.

The F.I.D.I.C. contract has evolved from the fourth edition of the I.C.E. conditions of contract and although the third edition of F.I.D.I.C. incorporates many of the same clause numbers and headings, similar wording and some of the changes in approach of the I.C.E. fifth edition, it does not include the more controversial additions and changes and therefore is substantially similar to the I.C.E. fourth edition. However, although there are many points of similarity between the two editions of the I.C.E. conditions of contract and the F.I.D.I.C. conditions, it should not be assumed that they are always applied in the same way.

The third edition of the F.I.D.I.C. conditions consists of several parts:– Part I – General Conditions, Part II – Conditions of Particular Application, Part III – Conditions of Particular Application to Dredging and Reclamation Work, a Form of Tender and a Form of Agreement. Part I is similar to the I.C.E. conditions of contract and the main differences are outlined below. Part II is a short list of those clauses which may require amendment to suit the particular contract circumstances and locality of the works and includes notes on the preparation of such amendments.

Clause 2 (1) covers a situation, unfortunately more common on overseas contracts, where the engineer has to obtain approval from the employer for carrying out his duties. Under these circumstances the sub-clause requires this fact to be set out in Part II of the conditions.

Clause 4 states that the engineer's consent to sub-letting shall not be unreasonably withheld.

The F.I.D.I.C. conditions are also available in official translations into French, German and Spanish and for overseas work the other contract documents might be written in these or other languages. Obviously it is necessary to state which languages are to be used and which language is definitive. For this purpose Clause 5 (1) requires the language or languages in which the contract documents are written to be stated in Part II, and if these documents are written in more than one language, the "Ruling Language" shall also be stated in Part II. The "Ruling Language" is the language in which the contract is to be construed and interpreted. A note of agreement is to be found inside the front cover of the third edition stating that the English version of the conditions shall be the official and authentic text for translation into any other language. It is important that the engineer's representative, the contractor's agent, the employer, and members of their staff are fluent in the language specified. For most contracts this language is unlikely to be the mother tongue of all these people and care should be taken to avoid misunderstandings. This advice also applies to translated documents and these should be checked by an independent translation back into the original language. The country or state whose law is to apply to the contract shall also be stated in Part II. In general this is likely to be the country in which the construction work is situated and if this is outside the Commonwealth in European influenced or Islamic countries where the legal system is not based on English Law, then great care should be taken in preparing the documents to suit local legal requirements.

Clause 11 requires soils and hydrological investigation data which have been obtained by the employer to be made available, and for the tender to be based on such data but with the contractor responsible for its interpretation.

Clause 12 does not contain the detailed procedures of the I.C.E. conditions.

Clause 13 generally retains the wording of the I.C.E. fourth edition and therefore omits reference to instructions resulting in delay and extra cost. Clause 14 is also more limited in scope than the fifth edition particularly regarding information about and consent to methods of construction.

The wording of the sub-clauses of Clause 34 differ from those in the I.C.E. fifth edition and take into account the somewhat different labour situation found overseas. For instance, the sub-clauses refer to supply of water, non supply of alcohol, drug and arms, observance of religious customs and festivals, epidemic illness and disorderly conduct, and allow for other conditions affecting labour and wages to be set out in Part II.

Clause 44 does not incorporate the additional provisions for interim and final assessments of extension of time for completion contained in the I.C.E. fifth edition. Clause 47 concerning liquidated damages for delay also retains the I.C.E. fourth edition wording; with the addition of a sub-clause providing for the payment of a bonus for early completion if this is set out in Part II, and omits completely the complicated provisions for liquidated damages for delay for sections of works contained in the fifth edition.

Clause 52 again retains a fourth edition flavour but with the addition of sub-clause 52 (3) which provides for adjustment of the contract price where the variations increase or decrease the net contract sum by more than 10 per cent. The detailed notice ... of claims procedures defined in the fifth edition have not been included. Clauses 53 and 54 concerning plant, temporary works and materials do not provide for these to be vested in the employer as do the clauses in the fifth edition. In addition Clause 53 refers to the employer's assistance in obtaining consent for re-export and customs clearance for plant.

Unlike Clause 58 of the fifth edition, the F.I.D.I.C. conditions only refer to provisional sums and not prime cost items. Clause 59 concerning nominated sub-contractors is less detailed than Clauses 59A and 59B in the fifth edition.

Clause 60 relating to certificates and payments has an additional sub-clause stating that the conditions of payment and repayment for advances on plant and materials shall be set out in Part II. A further sub-clause allows for a proportion of payments to be made in appropriate foreign currencies with the type of currency and rate of exchange to be stated in Part II. The provisions for payment, certificates, retention and interest have to be set out in Part II as there are no sub-clauses similar to those in the I.C.E. fifth edition.

Towards the end of the F.I.D.I.C. conditions the clause numbering varies from that in the fifth edition but the substance of the clauses is similar, except for Clauses 67, 69, 70, 71 and 72. Clause 67 concerning arbitration requires the settlement of disputes to be made under the rules of conciliation and arbitration of the International Chamber of Commerce and not under an arbitrator appointed by the President of the I.C.E. as the equivalent Clause 66 in the fifth edition.

Clause 69 relates to the default of the employer and entitles the contractor to terminate his employment after certain defined defaults. Clause 70 relates to price adjustments for increases or decreases in costs of labour and materials and requires these to be set out in Part II. Clauses 71 and 72 relate to currency restrictions and rates of exchange and provide for reimbursement or payment accordingly. There are no clauses in the fifth edition equivalent to the last four clauses.

Other Standard Forms of Contract for Overseas Work

The two standard forms of contract described above are intended to be used for works measured and valued using a bill of quantities and not for lump sum, target or cost plus types of contract. They are also largely based on English legal interpretation. However, many countries have substantially different legal systems and not all contracts incorporate the principle of remeasurement. Therefore many countries have their own standard conditions of contract and often require these to be used. These standard conditions are generally prepared by legal sections within government departments, but because of the nature of civil engineering construction, they usually include clauses which contain the substance of similar clauses in the F.I.D.I.C. or I.C.E. conditions of contract suitably amended to cover the particular commercial, religious and legal practices in these countries. Because any civil engineering contract should deal with similar matters to those covered by the I.C.E. contract, the comments and explanations contained in this book may be used to assist understanding of the conditions in these other contracts, provided that the differences between the particular standard contract and the I.C.E. contract are ascertained.

In Western Europe the competitive design tender procedure is not unusual, and is probably adopted most frequently in France. This method was briefly discussed in Chapter 3.[1] There is an historical reason for this divergence from United Kingdom practice. Civil engineering as we know it today originated in Britain. At the beginning of the industrial era British engineers supervised and designed the first civil engineering projects of modern design carried out in Western Europe, and a few of them were constructed by British contractors. However in European countries civil engineering contractors became established before the advent of the consulting engineer in private practice. In addition because of differences in the European legal system and possibly lack of sufficient trained men at the time, English Law and British remeasurement practices were not adopted. Today, in those parts of the world where the Anglo-Saxon approach is not yet used, fresh interest is being shown in British and American methods.

In the United States it is more usual, but not universal, for the design to be finalized and the detailing completed before tenders are called for. Great importance is attached to planning and progress techniques, and more emphasis is now being placed on this aspect of civil engineering contracts by British engineers.

[1] See p. 69.

The law in the majority of Commonwealth countries and in most of the United States is closely related to English law, but it must be emphasized that when dealing with contracts in these countries the engineer must familiarize himself with the differences between their laws and those of England. In the United States the approach differs between some of the states. The doctrine of frustration, a part there are few major deviations between the common law of England and the United States insofar as it affects contracts. The principal difference in practice in the United States is the provision by the promoter of bills of quantities.[1] The construction industry in the United States has initiated investigations into the possibility of the more extensive use of bills of quantities. It is hoped that the contractual practice explained in this book will provide a useful guide to those in the United States and elsewhere who desire to make more widely known the benefits that can be reaped by all parties by the employment of a usage similar to the English system of quantities and its related contract procedures.

---

[1] Standard Form of Contract used by U.S. Government; Standard Form of Contract issued by the American Railway Engineering Association for Lump Sum and Unit Price Contracts.

CROSS REFERENCES TO I.C.E. (5TH ED.), J.C.T. PRIVATE (WITH QUANTITIES), 1980 AND GC/WORKS/1 (EDITION 2)

Clause References

Clause	I.C.E.	J.C.T.	GC/Works/1	Comments
Abandonment of contract by contractor	63(1)	27	–	
Access to site workshops	37	11	13(2)	
Accident or injury to workmen	24	21	47	In J.C.T. and GC/works/1 contract workmen not specifically mentioned.
Admission to site	–	–	56,57	
Adverse physical conditions and artificial obstructions	12	–	–	
Agent	15(2)	10	33	The J.C.T. contract refers to a person-in-charge.
Agreement	9	–	–	
Antiquities	32	34	20(2)	Includes archaeological finds and fossils.

Clause	I.C.E.	J.C.T.	GC/Works/1	Comments
Arbitration	66	Art.5	61	Article 5 of the J.C.T. agreement deals with arbitration.
Assignment and sub-letting	3,4	19	27,30	I.C.E. contract states piece-work not subletting, refusal to allow subletting is conditional on it being reasonable in J.C.T. contract. I.C.E. and GC/Wks/1 both give power of unconditional refusal.
Bond	10	–	–	
Boreholes and exploratory excavations	18	–	–	
Breach of contract	63	27	–	
Certificates and payments	60,61,62	30	40,41,42	The I.C.E. contract provides for interest to be paid when the employer fails to honour the engineer's certificate. The G/C Works/1 contract allows for an interim advance midway between monthly valuations when contract sum exceeds £100,000.
Claims, notice of	52(4)	26	40(3),48	
Clearance of site on completion	33	–	–	

Clause	I.C.E.	J.C.T.	GC/ Works/1	Comments
Completion, certificate, time for completion	43,48	1,17,23,26	28,41,42	
Completion, sectional	43,47,48	18	–	
Completion agreement	9	1	–	I.C.E. contract explicitly states contract agreement to be at expense of employer.
Contract documents	5,6,7	2 Articles of agreement	4,5 5 A–B	
Contract, extent of	1,5,11	1	1	
Corrupt gifts	–	–	55	
Defective work and materials, removal of	39	8	13	
Definitions	1	1	1	
Delays, extension of time, liquidated damages	27(6), 44, 46,47	24,25,26	28,29,53	Cl. 46 allows the engineer to require the contractor to expedite the work when there is no reason to allow an extension of time
Determination of contract, for forfeiture	63	27,28	44,45,46	J.C.T. contract deals explicitly with contractor's power to determine. I.C.E. contract does not

Clause	I.C.E.	J.C.T.	GC/Works/1	Comments
Duties and powers of engineer's and architects' representatives	2	12	16	I.C.E. contract allows engineer to delegate considerable powers. J.C.T. contract empowers clerk of works to act solely as inspector of works.
Excavation, materials from	–	–	20	GC/Works/1 contract states that employer retains property in all excavated materials
Facilities for other contractors and tradesmen	31	29	50	
Final and maintenance certificates	60,61,62	30	41,42	
Fluctuations	Special conditions CPF CE/FSS	37,38,39 40	11A–G	These clauses are subject to revision. In the J.C.T. contract the different provisions are dealt with separately in Cl.38,39,40, which are published separately
Frustration	64	32	–	J.C.T. contract is concerned only with procedures resulting from causes due to war
Hidden works	38	–	9,21,22	
Highways and hedges and damage to roads	29,30, 49(5)	–	48	
Indemnities	20,22	20	26,27	
Inspection of site	11	–	2	

Clause	I.C.E.	J.C.T.	GC/Works/1	Comments
Instructions of engineer, architect superintending officer and variations	5,13,51, 52	4,14,25	7,8, 9,24	I.C.E. contract requires contractor to submit each month an account giving details of all claims for additional expense and of extra work. J.C.T. contract requires the contractor to make claim for expenses not otherwise reimbursable within a reasonable time.
Insurance of works	21,25	22	–	I.C.E. contract requires the contractor to insure the works. J.C.T. contains three clauses (two of which must be deleted) requiring either contractor or employer to insure the works, or for the works to be at the employer's risk. No obligation for contractor to insure in GC/Works/1 contract.
Insurance, third party and employer's liability	23,24,25	21	–	J.C.T. contract calls for a provisional sum to be included in the bill of quantities if required to cover cost of the promoter's third party risks.
Labour conditions	34	19A	35,41	I.C.E. Clause 34 was amended in 1983 to delete reference to Fair Wages Resolution and replaced it with reference to

Clause	I.C.E.	J.C.T.	GC/Works/1	Comments
				wage–rates conditions etc. in the Civil Engineering Working Rule Agreement (Amendment Sheet No.2 to I.C.E. contract (revised 1979))
Labour, returns of	35	–	34	
Liquidated damages	47	24	29	J.C.T. contract makes it mandatory for architect to issue a certificate should the works overrun the completion date, stating this. Enforcement of payment of damages at employer's discretion. Procedure complicated by possibility of extension of time being granted later.
Maintenance (defects liability period)	49,50	17	32,41	I.C.E. contract has sub-clause dealing with reinstatement of highway and roads.
Measurement, bills of quantities	1,6,55, 56,57	13,14	4,5, 37,39	I.C.E. contract assumes use of *Civil Engineering Standard Method of Measurement*, and visualizes the admeasurement of the whole contract. J.C.T. stipulates use of *Building Standard Method of Measurement*.

Clause	I.C.E.	J.C.T.	GC/Works/1	Comments
Metrication	71	–	–	
Nominated sub-contractors	58, 59A–C	35	31,38	J.C.T. contract gives two alternative methods of nomination with *alternative* tendering procedures. Nomination procedures can be avoided by measuring the sub-contract works and giving a list of not less than three firms. The contractor so selected would be a domestic sub-contractor. See Cl. 19 J.C.T. contract
Nominated suppliers	58, 59A–C	36	31,38	Terms for cash discount differ in each contract.
Notice and Fees	26,27	6	14	
Nuisance	29	–	18	
Ownership of unfixed materials and plants	53,54	16	3	
Programme to be furnished	14	–	–	
Progress, rate of	46	–	6	
Provisional and prime cost sums	58, 59A–C	35,36	39	
Removal of contractors employees	16	8	36	

Clause	I.C.E.	J.C.T.	GC/Works/1	Comments
Retention	60	30	30	
Schedule of rates	–	–	5A	See also J.C.T. contract (without quantities) Cl. 5 and 13
Scotland, application to	67	–	–	
Secrecy	–	–	58,59	
Service of notices	68	–	1	
Setting out	17	7	12	
Specification	–	–	4	
Superintendence to be provided by the contractor	15	10	33	
Sureties and performance bonds	10	–	–	
Suspension and postponement	40	23	23	GC/Works/1 contract suspension only for frost, etc.
Tax deductions	69	31	–	
Testing materials	36	8	13	
Urgent repairs	62	–	49	
Variations	51,52	4,13	9,10	Oral instructions must be confirmed in writing
War damage	65	33	–	
Watching and lighting	19	–	17	

EVENTS WHICH MAY JUSTIFY AN EXTENSION OF TIME UNDER THE I.C.E. CONTRACT

1. The adverse physical conditions mentioned in Cl. 12.
2. Exceptional adverse weather conditions (Cl. 44 (1)).
3. Variations (Cl. 51 (1), 44 (1)).
4. Failure of the engineer to issue drawings or instructions at reasonable times (Cl. 7 (3)).
5. Increase in quantities above those in the bills (Cl. 44 (1)).
6. Instructions or directions under Cl. 5 or Cl. 13 (1) (Cl. 14 (6)).
7. Delay of the engineer in consenting to the contractors proposed method of construction (Cl. 14 (6)).
8. Variations involving street works (Cl. 27 (6)).
9. Forfeiture of a nominated sub-contract (Cl. 59B (4)).
10. Failure to give possession of the site (Cl. 42 (1)).
11. Suspension of the progress of the works. (Cl. 40 (1)).
12. Affording facilities to other contractors (Cl. 31 (2)).
13. Other special circumstances which fairly entitle the contractor to an extension.

EVENTS WHICH MAY JUSTIFY AN EXTENSION OF TIME UNDER J.C.T. STANDARD FORM CONTRACTS

1. *Force majeure* (Cl. 25. 41).
2. Exceptionally adverse weather conditions (Cl. 25. 4. 2.).
3. Loss or damage occasioned by any one or more of the perils to be insured against and listed in Cl. 22 (25. 4. 3.).
4. Civil commotions, strikes affecting the works (25. 4. 4.).
5. Compliance with the architects' instructions (25. 4. 5.) under the following clauses:–
   2. 3.　Correcting discrepancies between documents
   8.　Opening up or testing of work which is in accordance with the contract
   13. 2.　Variations
   13. 3.　Expenditure of provisional sums
   23. 2　Postponement of any work
   34.　Discovery and presentation of antiquities
   35.　Nominated sub-contractors
   36.　Nominated suppliers.
6. Instructions not received in "due time" (Cl. 25. 4. 6.).
7. Delay by nominated sub-contractors or suppliers (24. 4. 7.).
8. Delay caused by persons directly employed or materials to be supplied by the employer (24. 4. 8.).
9. Government statutes etc. which directly affect the execution by restricting the use of labour or fuel etc. (25. 4. 9.).
10. The contractor's inability for reasons beyond his control, which he could not reasonably have foreseen at the date of tender, to secure labour or materials essential for the works (Cl. 25. 4. 10.).
11. Delay by a local authority or statutory undertaker in carrying out work (Cl. 25. 4. 11.).
12. Failure of the employer to give access to the site (Cl. 25. 4. 12.).

BIBLIOGRAPHY

Construction Economics

An Introduction to Engineering Economics, Institution of Civil Engineers, 1969.

Flanagan, R. and Norman, G., *Life Cycle Costing for Construction,* Royal Institution of Chartered Surveyors, 1983.

Stone P.A., *Building Economy,* 3rd Ed. 19 , Pergamon Press.

Critical Path Method

Lockyer, K.G., *Introduction to Critical Path Method,* Pitman, London.

O'Brian, J.J., *Scheduling Handbook,* McGraw-Hill.

Shaffer, L.R., Ritter, J.B., and Meyer, W.L., *The Critical Path Method,* McGraw-Hill.

Measurement and Specification

Barnes, M., *Measurement in Contract Control,* Institution of Civil Engineers, 1977.

Barnes, M., *Examples of the CESMM,* Institution of Civil Engineers, 1977.

Seeley, I.H., *Civil Engineering Quantities,* 3rd Ed., 1977, Macmillan.

Seeley, I.H., *Civil Engineering Specification,* 2nd Ed., 1977, Macmillan.

Practice and Procedure

Civil Engineering Procedure, 3rd Ed., 19 , Institute of Civil Engineers.

ICE Arbitration Procedure, 1983.

Guidance on Tenders for Civil Engineering Contracts, Thomas Telford, 1983.

Haswell, C.K., and de Silva, D.S., *Civil Engineering Contracts: Practice and Procedure,* Butterworth, 1982.

Willis and Willis, *Practice and Procedure for the Quantity Surveyor,* 6th Ed. 1976, Crosby Lockwood.

Law

(1) Building and Civil Engineering Law

Abrahamson, M., *Engineering Law and I.C.E. Contracts*, 4th Ed. Applied Science Publishers Ltd, 1979.

Cornes, D., *Design Liability in the Construction Industry*, 1983, Granada.

Emden, A.E. and Bickford-Smith, S. *et al.*, *Building Contracts and Practice*, 8th Ed., Butterworth, London, 1980.

Duncan Wallace, I.N., *Hudsons Building and Engineering Contracts*, 10th Ed. Sweet & Maxwell, London 1970. Supplement, 1979.

Keating, D., *Law and Practice of Building Contracts*, 4th Ed., Sweet & Maxwell, London 1980.

Uff, J., *Construction Law*, Sweet & Maxwell, 1978.

(2) Commentaries on Standard Forms of Construction Contracts

Duncan Wallace, I.N., *Building and Civil Engineering Standard Forms*, Sweet & Maxwell, London, 1969 with Supplement, 1970–73.

Duncan Wallace, I.N., *Further Building and Engineering Standard Forms*, Sweet & Maxwell, London, 1973.

Duncan Wallace, I.N., *The International Civil Engineering Contract*, Sweet & Maxwell, London, 1974, with supplement, 1980.

Porter, R., *Guide to Building Contract Conditions*, George Goodwin Ltd., 1980.

Sawyer, J.G. and Gillot, C.A., *The F.I.D.I.C. Conditions. Digest of contractual relationships and responsibilities.* Thomas Telford, 1981.

Duncan Wallace, I.N. *The International Civil Engineering Contract.* A Commentary on the F.I.D.I.C. International Standard Form of Civil Engineering and Building Contract, Sweet & Maxwell, 1974; with supplement 1980.

Duncan Wallace, I.N. *The I.C.E. Conditions of Contract*, 5th Ed., Sweet & Maxwell, 1978.

(3) Law of Contract Generally

Anson, Sir W.R. *Law of Contract*, 25th Ed. by A.G. Guest, Oxford University Press, 1979.

Cheshire, G.C. and Fifoot, C.H.S., *Law of Contract*, 10th Ed. Butterworths, London, 1981.

Treitel, G.H., *The Law of Contract*, 6th Ed., 1983. Stevens & Sons, London, 1975.

(4) Company Law

Charlesworth, I.J. and Cain, T.E., *Principles of Company Law*, 12th Ed. by T.E. Cain, Stevens & Sons, London, 1983.

(5) Private International Law

Cheshire, G.C. and North, P.M., *Private International Law*, 10th Ed., Butterworths, London, 1979

INDEX